CONE-BEARING TREES OF THE PACIFIC COAST

WHITTLESEY HOUSE FIELD GUIDE
SERIES

·◖ ◗·

Bowers · CONE-BEARING TREES OF THE PACIFIC
COAST

Harlow · TREES OF THE EASTERN UNITED STATES
AND CANADA

CONE-BEARING TREES

OF THE

PACIFIC COAST

BY

NATHAN A. BOWERS

B.Sc., C.E., Ph.D.

New York WHITTLESEY HOUSE *London*

M C G R A W - H I L L B O O K C O M P A N Y , I N C .

CONE-BEARING TREES OF THE PACIFIC COAST

Copyright, 1942, *by the* McGraw-Hill Book Company, Inc.

PUBLISHED BY WHITTLESEY HOUSE
A division of the McGraw-Hill Book Company, Inc.

Printed in the United States of America by The Maple Press Co., York, Pa.

PREFACE

In its original form the material in this manual was prepared as a convenient means of helping the author get better acquainted with cone-bearing trees of Pacific forests. Then he discovered that there were others, by no means botanists, who loved the forest trees and needed help in learning more about them. The common difficulty was a lack of effective aids. It seems strange that so little information is prepared for the nonbotanical lover of trees, this despite the many years in which scientists have been studying our forests, classifying the trees, and making painstaking and exhaustive records of what and where they are—all for those who understand botanical terms.

There is a need, the author believes, for something in between the technical treatise and the sketchy "popular" material that does not at all reflect the very exhaustive information locked up in technical records. Even though one was neither a botanist nor interested in a knowledge of botanical terminology, he still could know a great deal about trees, know their characteristic traits, learn to recognize them on sight, and find much pleasure in a close acquaintance with them. Was there not some way in which the information in the scientific records could be made available to the nonbotanical tree lover and thus help him attain this nontechnical and yet close acquaintance with the trees? In short, could not a field manual on conifers native to Pacific Coast forests be made comprehensive and definite without making it technical in a botanical sense?

To produce an affirmative answer to these questions was the task that the author set for himself in preparing the material here presented. He believes that there are many tree lovers who want and will use a manual made as comprehensive and complete as possible without botanical terms. This manual is designed to meet that need, and at the same time it is kept within the limits of what would be useful on mountain trips and in ramblings through forests of the Pacific slope.

This manual would not have been complete and would have fallen far short of the objective without the drawings of needles and cones for each species that originally appeared in "Forest Trees of the Pacific Slope" by George B. Sudworth, dendrologist, U.S. Forest Service. The author gratefully acknowledges the help of the Forest Service not only in preparing these drawings for reproduction but in supplying photographs of many species.

John A. Lee of Portland, by his own diligent study of trees and his persevering effort to get together information that the layman could understand and use in identification, was an inspiring influence as well as an unfailing source of encouragement. He also supplied numerous ideas and special methods useful in identification. These results of his own careful and observant study have not been published heretofore. Much credit, therefore, is due Mr. Lee and is gratefully acknowledged.

George D. Whittle made special effort, over a period of years, to obtain representative pictures of tree species that were not otherwise readily available. O. E. Stanley made a search through "high places" of the Northwest for a suitable frontispiece subject and made the color photograph from which the frontispiece is reproduced. Botanist John Thomas Howell of the Academy of Sciences supplied much helpful advice with reference to all parts of the manual and assembled all the data on the cypresses.

To numerous other friends who have contributed from their personal collections pictures that were not available elsewhere, the author expresses his thanks and appreciation.

NATHAN A. BOWERS.

ATHERTON, CALIF.

CONTENTS

CONE-BEARING TREES OF THE
PACIFIC COAST

Directions for Use of This Manual

IN THESE directions reference is made to the "student" rather than to the "reader" because the manual is designed for use more as a dictionary or a field text than as a book to be *read* in the ordinary sense. It is assumed that the person who uses this manual will expect it to aid him in identifying different species of conifers and in studying and comparing their characteristics so that he can recognize them on sight. If he would accomplish this, he should first familiarize himself with the general arrangement of the material in the manual, which he will find in two forms, as follows:

1. A map, keys, and tabulations which group the trees in different classifications. Considered collectively these might be called the general aids. They enable the student to decrease the number of species with which he must concern himself in making final identification of any particular tree. In fact, when the student is trying to identify some tree that is new to him, these general aids should enable him to reduce to a small number —perhaps to only three or four—the species that he will need to study in detail. All the foregoing are in the first part of the book; then come:

2. Complete descriptions of distinguishing features of each species, arranged in a uniform order to facilitate comparisons. The detailed descriptions, 56 in number, are in alphabetical order and are accompanied by pictures of the trees themselves and scale drawings of needles and cones. The major portion of the manual is devoted to these descriptions because from them the student will get the detailed information that will make him really conversant with the different species. This information has been boiled down into what actually will be useful in distinguishing and identifying; endeavor has been made to avoid anything not pertinent to this aim. The pictures, likewise,

were selected with preference for those which emphasize distinctive traits. For example, in the case of the Western Larch a general view of the entire tree showing the remarkably tall, slender shape obviously is most informative. In the case of the Sitka Spruce, on the other hand, a general view would not do at all because it would resemble too closely the general views of several other trees. The Sitka Spruce picture of most aid to the student is a close-up emphasizing the peculiar base of the tree with the much-enlarged butt section and the characteristic bark form.

Before giving a practical example to illustrate the most effective use of the manual, the student's attention is directed to the three keys: needle key, elevation key, and geographical key. These immediately follow the directions, and the student should familiarize himself with them at the outset. A description printed with each key (where it will be convenient for reference should the student need to refresh his memory from time to time) explains the arrangement of keys and how they are to be used.

All the keys list the trees alphabetically by index number, and in the detailed descriptions this same designation is printed on each page for convenience in cross references. For example, when interested in the Limber Pine the student will save much time by looking for its index number, "P-14," whether he is using one of the keys or that portion of the manual devoted to detailed descriptions. The "P" indicates that the tree is a pine; the "14" is its individual number in the pine group.

Identifying a tree as belonging to a particular species is largely a recognition of characteristic traits that other species do not have. Therefore the beginner is helped most by aids that eliminate as many as possible of the similar species with which he might confuse the tree under consideration. The keys are quick and convenient means of doing just this. They are arranged to be used jointly. One key alone may be sufficient for identification in some cases, but more often it is necessary to go farther. An excellent habit in examining some species of conifer new to the student is to check through all three keys and then read the detailed descriptions of those trees which the keys indicate to be possibilities.

Now for a practical illustration of how to use the manual. Suppose that the student is in northern California (say in the

Trinity Alps, south of the Klamath River) at an elevation somewhere between 6,000 and 7,000'. He may not know the exact elevation, but he will know within a thousand feet or so, and that will be close enough. He finds here a cone-bearing tree with needles grouped in bundles of three, averaging 8 to 10" long. His procedure in identifying this tree by the use of the manual would be as follows:

Turning first to the needle key he looks for the table listing trees whose needles are in bundles of three. He finds six trees so listed. Turning now to the elevation key he finds that of the six, three (Knobcone Pine, P-6; Digger Pine, P-7; and Monterey Pine, P-8) can be eliminated because they are low-level trees listed only in elevation zone 1 and hence would not be found at elevation 6,000' or higher. Now checking the geographical distribution (last column of the elevation key) of the remaining three trees, he finds that one (Bigcone Pine, P-13) does not occur north of district I. So he turns to the map in the geographical key and finds that Bigcone Pine can be eliminated because district I is far to the south of the location in which his "unknown" was found.

Thus, within a very short space of time, by consulting the keys he has reduced the possibilities to two species: Western Yellow Pine, P-2, and Jeffrey Pine, P-3. The keys now have fulfilled their function, and the student turns to the detailed descriptions of P-2 and P-3, where he will find information about cone sizes and other specific features which should be studied carefully to make distinction between these two very similar species.

In addition to their great value in this process of quick elimination, the keys are well worth frequent review to keep distinctions clearly in mind. The manual as a whole, in fact, has been designed for use in the woods, and the habit of referring to it often while examining trees will fix characteristic traits in mind in such a way that the student will become adept in recognizing different species as he sees them.

Once their traits are known, some species can be recognized with certainty even from a considerable distance, though obviously this holds only for those whose characteristic traits are such that they are visible at a distance. After a little study and experience the student may expect to recognize perhaps eight or ten species from a distance by the general shape of tree, the color, the density of foliage, or other sharply distinctive features. Then comes a much larger group—perhaps twenty-five or thirty species—which the amateur naturalist can expect to identify only after somewhat closer inspection and perhaps with the aid of field glasses to note the location, shape, and position of cones. Finally, there remains that fascinating group of fifteen or twenty species which he can identify positively only after having opportunity to handle, measure, and study needles and cones carefully, frequently consulting his reference data to avoid being misled by corresponding traits of other trees whose characteristics are similar.

Since the manual is decidedly not for the botanist, the original plan was to omit botanical names and terms entirely. That was not advisable because confusion would be sure to result if the student had no recourse when confronted with the same names (Bull Pine, Jack Pine, etc.) applied to different species in different localities. This risk of confusion is avoided by using the botanical names for indexing and for reference. The most popular of the common names is always given with the botanical name for the convenience of the student. A very few botanical terms also have been introduced where they will be enough of a convenience to the student to make it worth his while to learn them. These terms, which are defined in the glossary at the back of the manual, and the botanical names are not nearly so formidable as they look; there are not many to be learned; and once the student becomes familiar with them, he will find much pleasure in the convenience that their use will prove to be. If distinction between "genus" and "species" is not perfectly clear, definitions of these terms in the glossary should be studied at the outset.

After a little time spent in study of the manual, trees that the student at first found hard to distinguish are seen to have characteristic traits that were unnoticed before. There is great satisfaction in finding that you readily recognize as friends conifers which were strangers until you learned the numerous little signs by which they show their individuality.

What to Observe

RECOGNITION is based on memory of appearance. With a little study to acquire knowledge of what details to observe plus a little experience in applying it, anyone can know and quickly recognize our native conifers. In this chapter the purpose is to make practical suggestions on how to go about examining an "unknown" tree in a systematic way. Experienced observers doubtless will have their own well-developed systems. The need of beginners has been emphasized to the author by the meager information brought in by friends who want to know the identity of certain trees that they have examined. Sometimes they have only vague descriptions; their specific data is largely on unimportant points; and really essential features have been missed altogether. This despite the fact that there was ample time and opportunity to observe significant traits plus a sincere desire to do so.

A systematic plan for observing characteristic traits not only will help the student identify trees that are new to him but will increase the speed and certainty of his recognition of species with which he already has slight acquaintance.

The Distant View

Traits that may be observed easily and quickly are those rather obvious ones which can be seen from afar. Trees of some species do not have such traits; others have distinguishing features in (1) shape, (2) color, or (3) foliage that can be recognized a long way off. To illustrate by example, typical instances of these three traits are cited in the following:

1. The shape of the Digger Pine is distinctive in that in 90 per cent of the trees the trunk separates some distance above the ground into several major parts of nearly the same size and importance. This peculiarity can be distinguished as far as the

tree can be seen. Again, the shape of the mature Redwood is distinctive in the graceful, *downward* sweep of its branches. In older Redwoods the tops frequently are flat because the leading tip has a tendency to die out as the tree ages. These two shape features make the species stand out distinctly from among the Douglas Firs with which it frequently associates. Not in every case, but frequently, this shape characteristic will suggest "Redwood" long before one comes close enough for other and more definite proofs of identity.

2. A color example occurs in the cinnamon-red bark of the mature Western Yellow Pine and the Western Red Cedar. This striking color instantly catches the eye because it stands out in sharp distinction from other forest colors. There is no risk of confusing these two species through this similarity of distinctive colorings; the Cedar bark is composed of long, stringy ridges, whereas bark of the Western Yellow Pine forms large, flat plates.

3. Foliage is sometimes markedly distinctive, as in the case of the Digger Pine. This species has long, thin needles that tend to separate and are loosely hung among the branches. The result has been well described by saying that this is a tree that one can literally "see through."

When leaving a tree that has been examined for the first time an excellent plan is to look back at it from time to time while walking away, thus comparing the distant view with what has been observed close up and fixing in mind any traits of shape, color, etc., that can be discerned from a distance.

Foliage

Of the traits that call for close inspection the first is the foliage classification described in the needle key. In examining needles it is well to be sure that the preponderant grouping is noted; this means looking at a sufficient number to make certain that the count used in referring to the key is really representative and not different from the majority.

After deciding (with the aid of the needle key) on the particular group in which the new tree belongs, one can observe many more details on the subject of foliage. It is helpful to jot down the observations in a notebook. The experienced observer will have his own list of items that he finds particularly useful. For the beginner who may need a little help on this point, here are a few suggestions.

If the foliage is scale-like, note whether the pattern is (1) fern-like, *i.e.*, having an "elk-horn" or flat pattern formation as in the cedars, or (2) made up of separate, similar, scale-covered twigs as in the cypresses. If of the second type, note the cross-section to see whether it is square or rounded. Note whether the foliage is soft to the touch or sharp and prickly, also if it has a strong odor when bruised.

In examining needles there is much to be observed after the first question of "number per bundle" has been answered. Note the average length; this is important. For the length measurement do not select needles on the leader, at the tips of branchlets where they are immature, or on the branches where they may have remained beyond maturity. Select needles on typical branchlets where they are growing in the manner that you observe to be characteristic of the tree.

Note whether the characteristic growth of the needles is (1) in tufts, well toward the end of the branchlets; (2) spaced uniformly along the full length of branchlets; (3) in flat, two-ranked sprays; (4) bristling radially in all directions from the twigs; or (5) twisting from the lower side to join those above and thus giving a brush-like formation.

Note whether the cross-section of needles is (1) flat, (2) triangular, (3) rectangular, or (4) circular. If they are flat, are they ribbed and does the underside have a whitish appearance contrasting with the dark green of the upper side? Are they curved or straight, stiff or soft and flexible, and are the tips sharp, blunt, or notched?

Observations of all these points may seem a cumbersome process at first; but as the student adds to his knowledge of characteristic traits, he will associate various features of this sort with the different species and instinctively will look for them to confirm the identity suggested by more obvious traits that were seen first.

The pines—all 17 of them—have needles whose bundles are circular in cross-section. In those attached in bundles of two the section of each of the two needles in the bundle will be found to be an exact semicircle, making a perfectly complete circle when the two are held together. The bundles of threes, fours, and fives will be found to be made up of thirds, fourths, and fifths, respectively, of a true circle. Of the 17 pines only one species has needles attached singly (instead of in bundles), and in this one (Singleleaf Pine, P-16) each needle has a full circular section. Once you have fixed in mind this family trait of the pines by actual observations on needles of several species, you will feel that you have a personal acquaintance with a distinctive trait.

With many species of conifers the student will soon become so well acquainted that no close inspection will be necessary; his recognition will be quick and on first sight. Other species, particularly among the firs, are too similar in general appearance to permit of quick identification, and close examination will be necessary.

Cones

Cones are the most important items in the process of identifying different species of conifers from the point of view of the botanist. Not so with the nonbotanist; he may be unable to interpret distinctions, concealed within the cone, which the expert could find. Another reason for placing less emphasis upon them in this manual is the fact that one who is only a casual and occasional forest visitor may never have opportunity to handle and carefully examine cones of certain species—they may be far beyond reach if, indeed, he is able to find any at all even with the aid of binoculars. No cones of the true firs will be found on the ground; they fall apart when mature, leaving the central spine or stem remaining on the tree.

Nevertheless there is much to be learned from cones, and the student should turn his attention to them after the foliage has been carefully observed. Information about cones should be noted along the following lines:

Do they grow in an upright or pendant position? What is their size? Are they only near the top of the tree, or do they appear on the tips of many branches? Do they grow in clusters or singly? What is the color of the immature cones? (Not all young cones are green; in certain species they are purple before they open.)

If cones can be reached on the branches or if they can be picked up under the tree (cones do not necessarily belong to the

tree under which they are found), it is well to note the scales—
are they thick and strong or thin and papery? Do the scales
stand out in a fully opened position, or are some of them still
closed? What is the size of the seeds? Do they have papery
"wings" and if so of what size and shape? How many seeds
are under each fertile cone scale? (The number of seeds may
vary from 1 in some of the pines to 15 or 20 in the cypresses.)

It is a long way from the tiny "berry-like" cone of the junipers
to the cone of the Sugar Pine which may be 20″ long; similarly
there is a wide range from the paper-like cones of the spruce to
the strong, heavy form typical of the Jeffrey Pine. Several
species of pine cones have bracts—thin, leaf-like formations
between the scales. Douglas Fir cones have protruding bracts
of a peculiar three-pointed form that is not likely to be forgotten
once it has been observed carefully. There is only one other
bract at all similar, and that occurs in a species producing a larger
cone. Thus, this trait of the Douglas Fir makes it possible to
identify the species positively even from a cone that may have
been repeatedly crushed by automobile wheels—despite having
been battered out of shape, the peculiar three-pointed bract
is likely to be still in evidence and hence an almost certain indica-
tion of the species.

The student will do well to look up cone traits for trees of the
species that he expects to see on a certain trip and then make
observations in the field for comparison.

Bark and Other Characteristics

The bark of conifers varies widely, and bark characteristics
should be noted carefully. Young trees do not have the same
bark traits as do mature trees, and the latter are the more important. However, in some species young trees have important
bark indications, e.g., the blister-like resin pockets just beneath
the smooth bark surface of young firs.

When examining the bark of a mature tree, make notations
about color and thickness, the nature of the surface (whether
firm or covered with loose, scaly flakes, etc.), and whether the
formation is in large plates, as in the Western Yellow Pine, or
has the fibrous, stringy character of Redwood and Western
Red Cedar.

Features of the tree itself are important. What is its general shape—does it have the tall, narrow form of the Western Larch, or is it a scraggly, scrubby tree like the cypresses? Foliage and color are part of the general appearance of the tree. Note any tendency of the branches to turn upward or downward, especially at the tips, and whether the trunk is a single, straight stem for its full length, as in the firs, or has major divisions as in the Digger Pine. The Alaska Spruce, for example, has a trunk that tapers very rapidly just above the ground by reason of strong, buttress-like formations that connect roots and trunk—such traits are important indications. There may be various other distinctive characteristics about the base of the tree: better look and see.

Many conifers have peculiar little earmarks and signs by which they will be known to those who have observed them closely. The gracefully curving tips and lighter color of the Mountain Hemlock branchlets; the rigid, uniform regularity of upper branches in young Noble Fir; and the smooth, lacy appearance of Sugar Pine foliage are all typical of the rather intangible indications more easily observed than described. These traits the student will come to know so well that he will recognize them instantly if he will *form the habit of observation.*

REFERENCES AND ABBREVIATIONS

REFERENCES CITED

AUTHOR	ABBRE-VIATION	BOOK TITLE, PUBLISHER, AND DATE
George B. Sudworth	Su	"Forest Trees of the Pacific Slope," Government Printing Office, 1908
Charles Sprague Sargent	Sgt	"Manual of the Trees of North America," Houghton Mifflin Company, 1933
William M. Harlow and Ellwood S. Harrar	HH	"Textbook of Dendrology," McGraw-Hill Book Company, Inc., 1937
Canadian Forest Service	Can	"Native Trees of Canada," King's Printer, Ottawa, Can., 1933
Charles H. Shinn	Sh	"Let's Know Some Trees," *U.S. Dept. Agric. Misc. Circ.* 31, December, 1931
George W. Peavy	P	"Oregon's Commercial Forests," Oregon State Board of Forestry, 1929
J. Smeaton Chase	Ch	"Cone Bearing Trees of the California Mountains," A. C. McClurg & Company, 1911
James B. Berry	Be	"Western Forest Trees," World Book Company, 1926
Walter Fry and John R. White	FW	"Big Trees," Stanford University Press, 1930
W. L. Jepson	J	"The Trees of California," Sather Gate Book Shop, Berkeley, Calif., 1923
James Clifford Shirley	S	"The Redwoods of Coast and Sierra," University of California Press, 1937
John A. Lee*	JL	
George J. Young†	GY	

* Attorney (mountaineer-naturalist).

† Mining engineer (mountaineer-naturalist).

Abbreviations of authors' names, with page references, appear at the bottom of pages in that portion of the manual devoted to detailed descriptions of the species.

ABBREVIATIONS USED

★	A primary identification feature
′	Feet
″	Inches
Spec.	Species found exclusively in California

LIST OF TREE GROUPS

ALPHABETICALLY BY INDEX LETTERS

(Index in back of book)

BOTANICAL NAME	COMMON NAME	INDEX LETTER
Chamaecyparis	False Cedar	C
Chamaecyparis Lawsoniana	Port Orford Cedar	C-1
Chamaecyparis nootkatensis	Alaska Cedar	C-2
Libocedrus decurrens	Incense cedar	C-3
Thuja plicata	Western Red Cedar	C-4
Cupressus	Cypress	Cy
Cupressus macrocarpa	Monterey Cypress	Cy-1
Cupressus Goveniana	Gowen Cypress	Cy-2
Cupressus pygmaea	Dwarf Cypress	Cy-3
Cupressus Macnabiana	Macnab Cypress	Cy-4
Cupressus Forbesii	Tecate Cypress	Cy-5
Cupressus nevadensis	Piute Cypress	Cy-6
Cupressus Sargentii	Sargent Cypress	Cy-7
Abies	Fir	F
Abies lasiocarpa	Alpine Fir	F-1
Abies concolor	White Fir	F-2
Abies grandis	Grand Fir	F-3
Abies magnifica	California Red Fir	F-4
Abies nobilis	Noble Fir	F-5
Abies amabilis	Silver Fir	F-6
Abies venusta	Bristlecone Fir	F-7
Tsuga	Hemlock	H
Tsuga heterophylla	Western Hemlock	H-1
Tsuga Mertensiana	Mountain Hemlock	H-2
Pseudotsuga	False Hemlock	HF
Pseudotsuga taxifolia	Douglas Fir	Hf-1
Pseudotsuga macrocarpa	Bigcone Spruce	Hf-2
Juniperus	Juniper	J
Juniperus communis	Dwarf Juniper	J-1
Juniperus scopulorum	Rocky Mountain Juniper	J-2
Juniperus occidentalis	Western Juniper	J-3
Juniperus utahensis	Utah Juniper	J-4
Juniperus californica	California Juniper	J-5
Larix	Larch	L
Larix occidentalis	Western Larch	L-1
Larix Lyalli	Alpine Larch	L-2
Larix laricina	Tamarack	L-3
Pinus	Pines	P
Pinus Lambertiana	Sugar Pine	P-1
Pinus ponderosa	Western Yellow Pine	P-2
Pinus Jeffreyi	Jeffrey Pine	P-3
Pinus contorta	Lodgepole Pine	P-4

LIST OF TREE GROUPS.—*(Continued)*

BOTANICAL NAME	COMMON NAME	INDEX LETTER
Pinus monticola	Western White Pine	P-5
Pinus attenuata	Knobcone Pine	P-6
Pinus Sabiniana	Digger Pine	P-7
Pinus radiata	Monterey Pine	P-8
Pinus muricata	Pricklecone Pine	P-9
Pinus aristata	Bristlecone Pine	P-10
Pinus albicaulis	White-bark Pine	P-11
Pinus Torreyana	Torrey Pine	P-12
Pinus Coulteri	Bigcone Pine	P-13
Pinus flexilis	Limber Pine	P-14
Pinus Balfouriana	Foxtail Pine	P-15
Pinus monophylla	Singleleaf Pine	P-16
Pinus cembroides var. *Parryana*	Fourleaf Pine	P-17
Picea	Spruce	S
Picea Engelmannii	Engelmann Spruce	S-1
Picea sitchensis	Sitka Spruce	S-2
Picea Breweriana	Weeping Spruce	S-3
Picea Mariana	Black Spruce	S-4
Picea glauca	White Spruce	S-5
Sequoia	Sequoia	Se
Sequoia gigantea	Big Tree	Se-1
Sequoia sempervirens	Redwood	Se-2

Yews

(These are not true cone bearers but their close resemblance to them plus the fact that they have leaves in needle form suggests including them to avoid possible confusion in the student's mind.)

Torreya californica	California Nutmeg	To
Taxus brevifolia	Western Yew	Y

Total: 56 kinds of trees, including the two yews

How to Use the Needle Key

In the needle key the various species of conifers are grouped according to the peculiarities of their foliage. There are two primary distinctions, namely, whether the foliage occurs in the form of (1) needles or (2) scales. Needles are further subdivided into six groups according to the manner in which they are attached to the branchlets. The attachments may be singly; in bundles of twos, threes, fours, fives; or in clusters (no conifers of this region have a characteristic grouping in bundles of more than five). Finally, to a considerable extent there is a distinguishing trait in the average length of needles in each species, and hence the key gives the typical length range of needles.

When needle grouping (*i.e.*, the number of needles per bundle) and average needle length of any specimen have been observed, reference to the needle key will at once indicate the group in which the tree belongs. These simple observations on the needles of some tree new to the student, with the use of the needle key, often will reduce the possible classifications to 10 per cent of the total number of conifers. Because this long stride toward identification can be so quickly made with the needle key and because even the most inexperienced student can use it easily, the needle key is an excellent place to start the process of identification.

Within certain limits the grouping of needles varies, notably in the pines, and bundles containing two, three, or five needles may occur on the same twig. For example, although needles of the Sugar Pine (P-1) ordinarily are arranged in bundles of five, quite a few threes and twos may be found and rarely even bundles of four. The Monterey Pine (P-8) is the most extreme example of this departure from the preponderant arrangement; sometimes it will have a considerable percentage of its needles arranged in bundles of two. (See note under "Needles" in detailed description of P-8.)

Fortunately for the beginner, in most trees departures from the usual needle grouping are not numerous enough to be a problem, and with ordinary diligence in using the other keys in connection with the needle key he can make his identification with confidence. A safe rule to follow in examining some tree with which the student is not familiar is to be sure to ascertain the number of needles per bundle that is the preponderant arrangement. If this is done, there will be little risk of confusion in use of the needle key, and it will become one of the quickest and most convenient aids in distinguishing the different species.

NEEDLE KEY

Attached singly

		Length, inches
F	All seven firs	$2\frac{1}{2}$ max.
S	All five spruces	$1''$ max.
H-1	Western Hemlock	$\frac{1}{4}$–$1''$
H-2	Mountain Hemlock	$1''$ max.
Hf-1	Douglas Fir	1
Hf-2	Bigcone Spruce	1
J-1	Dwarf Juniper	$\frac{3}{4}''$ max.
P-16	Singleleaf Pine	$\frac{1}{2}$–2
Se-2	Redwood	$\frac{1}{2}$–1
To	Calif. Nutmeg	$1\frac{1}{4}$–$2\frac{1}{2}$
Y	Western Yew	$\frac{1}{2}$–1
	(Total 21)	

In bundles of 2

		Length, inches
P-4	Lodgepole Pine	1–3
P-9	Pricklecone Pine	$3\frac{1}{2}$–$5\frac{1}{2}$
	(Total 2)	

In bundles of 3

		Length, inches
P-2	Western Yellow Pine	4–11
P-3	Jeffrey Pine	8
P-6	Knobcone Pine	3–7
P-7	Digger Pine	7–13
P-8	Monterey Pine	3–6
P-13	Bigcone Pine	$6\frac{1}{2}$–12
	(Total 6)	

In bundles of 4

		Length, inches
P-17	Fourleaf Pine	$\frac{3}{4}$–$1\frac{5}{8}''$

In bundles of 5

		Length, inches
P-1	Sugar Pine	2–4
P-5	Western White Pine	1–4
P-10	Bristlecone Pine	$1\frac{1}{4}$–$1\frac{1}{2}$
P-11	White-bark Pine	1–$2\frac{1}{2}$
P-12	Torrey Pine	7–12
P-14	Limber Pine	$1\frac{1}{2}$–3
P-15	Foxtail Pine	$6\frac{3}{4}$–12
	(Total 7)	

Needles in clusters

		Length, inches	No. of needles per cluster
L-1	Western Larch	1–$1\frac{1}{2}$	14–30
L-2	Alpine Larch	1–$1\frac{5}{8}$	30–40
L-3	Alaska Larch	$\frac{7}{8}$–$1\frac{1}{8}$	12–20
	(Total 3)		

Scale-like foliage

Cy	All seven cypresses
J	Four of the five junipers
C-1	Port Orford Cedar
C-2	Alaska Cedar
C-3	Incense Cedar
C-4	Western Red Cedar
Se-1	Big Tree
	(Total 16)

GRAND TOTAL   56

How to Use the Elevation Key

THE elevation key consists of tables in which the conifers are classified according to the elevation range in which they naturally occur. The table is in three parts, namely, zones 1, 2, and 3, because three are not too many for the student to use easily and fewer than three would lose the advantage of many natural elevation groupings. In the zone 1 table are listed trees usually found below elevations of about 3,000'; zone 2 includes those which ordinarily occur somewhere between 3,000 and 5,000' (or a little higher); and in zone 3 are those whose range includes elevations above 6,000'. Some trees, like Lodgepole Pine, will be found listed in all three zones; others are limited to an elevation range of only a few hundred feet.

In the zone classification the exact fixing of elevation limits is not intended nor is it necessary. When the student wishes to identify a tree found at a stated elevation, as elevation 1,000' or elevation 2,000', there is great advantage in being able to eliminate quickly all species that grow only above, say, elevation 3,000'. Or, if he is at elevation 10,000', he can greatly simplify his problem of identification if he can concentrate attention on those which grow only at high levels. If a tree occurs in more than one zone, the other zones are listed in the second column of each table; altitude range is more exactly given in the fourth column. If the student is examining specimens near the border line between two zones, he will do well to consult both zone listings.

In the elevation tables the distribution of the trees is also indicated by letters that refer to belts or districts used in the geographical key. This is to simplify cross reference between elevation and geographical keys. For example, the letters A to L appearing in the fifth column mean that the tree is found in the districts from A to L inclusive as marked on the map that goes with the geographical key. The use of the tree grouping by districts is explained in detail in the directions for use of the geographical key.

The elevation range of conifers naturally trends to higher levels toward the South. For example, a certain species that grows best at elevations of 2,000 to 3,000′ in British Columbia probably will not find climatic conditions to its liking in southern California at less than 8,000 to 10,000′. It is natural that the farther south one goes the higher he would expect to find those trees which have a rather limited elevation range.

To give the student a more definite basis for placing a species in its proper elevation range, location is also mentioned in addition to the elevation range wherever danger of confusion might arise as a result of the tendency to range lower in the North and higher in the South. For example, instead of saying that a certain species will be found from sea level to 10,000′, if the fact is that this specimen grows at sea level in Alaska and at elevation 10,000′ in southern California, a more exact elevation rating is made possible by selecting some mid-latitude location, such as Oregon or Washington, and giving a definite elevation range for this latitude. Where this is done in this manual, notation always has been made to the effect that the elevation mentioned applies to the particular location named. The tree then is placed in the table corresponding to the elevation range in the latitude named.

Thus, where the student finds in the elevation key the notation "0 to 5,000′ *in Oregon,*" he will understand that a certain location is thus mentioned because in other latitudes there will be a different range—lower to the north, higher to the south.

ELEVATION ZONE 1

Conifers found at low elevations: *BELOW* 3,000′
(Including those whose upper range limit is usually 3,000′)

INDEX NO.	OTHER ELEV. ZONES	COMMON NAME	USUAL ELEV. RANGE, FT.	GEOGRAPHICAL DISTRIBUTION
C-1	2	Port Orford Cedar	Not above 5,000	FGH; Coos Bay, Ore., to Humboldt Co., Calif. (chiefly along coast)
C-3	2,3	Incense Cedar	1,000 to 5,000 in Oregon	F to L; So. Alaska to Central California
C-4	2,3	Western Red Cedar	0 to 7,500	A to I; So. Alaska to No. California
Cy-1	—	Monterey Cypress	0 to 100	J; on headlands of Monterey Bay
Cy-2	—	Gowen Cypress	200 to 500	J; same as Cy-1; farther inshore
Cy-3	—	Pygmy Cypress	200 to 1,000	I; along ocean in Mendocino Co., Calif.
Cy-4	—	Macnab Cypress	1,000 to 2,000	GHI; forms a "horseshoe" around north end of Sacramento Valley
Cy-5	2	Tecate Cypress	700 to 4,200	KL; in mountains of San Diego and Orange Counties, Calif.
Cy-7	—	Sargent Cypress	200 to 2,500	HIJ; Coast Range Mts., Mendocino to San Luis Obispo Counties
F-3	—	Grand Fir	0 to 3,000 in Oregon	A to I; Brit. Columbia to Ft. Ross, Calif. (a lowland tree)
F-6	2	Silver Fir	1,000 to 5,000	A to G; So. Alaska to Crater Lake, Ore.
H-1	2,3	Western Hemlock	0 to 7,000	A to I; Alaska to Marin Co., Calif. (not in Siskiyous)
Hf-1	2,3	Douglas Fir	0 to 7,000 or more	A to L; Canada to No. Mexico
Hf-2	2	Bigcone Spruce	1,500 to 6,000	KL; So. and Lower California
J-2	2	Rocky Mountain Juniper	0 to 6,500 in Oregon	B to G; Canada to Mexico
J-5	2	California Juniper	2,000 to 4,000	I to L *spec.*; Central California to No. Lower California
L-3	—	Tamarack	0 to 1,600	A; Alaska to Bering Sea
P-2	2,3	Western Yellow Pine	0 to 7,000 in Oregon	C to L; So. Brit. Columbia to No. Mexico
P-4	2,3	Lodgepole Pine	0 to 11,000	A to L; Alaska to Lower California
P-5	2,3	Western White Pine	0 to 10,000	B to K; Brit. Columbia to So. California
P-6	—	Knobcone Pine	1,500 to 3,000	G to L; S.W. Oregon to So. California (in dry mountain regions)
P-7	—	Digger Pine	500 to 4,000	H to K *spec.*; Sacramento Canyon to Tehachapi
P-8	—	Monterey Pine	Not above a few hundred feet	J; three arboreal islands: (1) Monterey; (2) San Simeon; (3) Guadaloupe Is.
P-9	—	Pricklecone Pine	0 to 1,000	I to L; Mendocino Co. to San Luis Obispo, Calif. (also on islands— max. 1 mi. inland)
P-12	—	Torrey Pine	Not above 100	L; two arboreal islands: (1) San Diego and (2) Santa Rosa Is.
P-13	2	Bigcone Pine	2,500 to 6,000	I to L; north side of Mt. Diablo to Lower California
S-2	—	Sitka Spruce	1,000 to 2,000	A to I; No. Alaska to No. California (max. 50 mi. inland)
S-4	—	Black Spruce	Swamplands	A; not south of Alaska in Pacific territory
Se-2	—	Redwood	0 to 2,500	G to J; So. Oregon to Monterey, Calif. (max. 30 mi. inland)
To	2	California Nutmeg	0 to 6,000	I to K *spec.*; Lake and Mendocino to Kern Counties
Y	2,3	Western Yew	0 to 6,000	A to I; Alaska to Central California

ELEVATION ZONE 2

Conifers usually *not below* 3,000′ *or above* 5,000 *or* 6,000′

INDEX NO.	OTHER ELEV. ZONES	COMMON NAME	USUAL ELEV. RANGE, FT.	GEOGRAPHICAL DISTRIBUTION
C-1	1	Port Orford Cedar	Not above 5,000	FGH; Coos Bay, Ore., to Humboldt Co., Calif. (chiefly along coast)
C-2	3	Alaska Cedar	2,000 to 7,500 in Washington	A to G; So. Alaska to the Siskiyous
C-3	1,3	Incense Cedar	1,000 to 5,000 in Oregon	F to L; So. Alaska to Central California
C-4	1,3	Western Red Cedar	0 to 7,500	A to I; So. Alaska to No. California
Cy-5	1	Tecate Cypress	700 to 4,200	KL; in mountains of San Diego and Orange Counties
Cy-6	—	Piute Cypress	4,000	J; on Piute Mt. near Bakersfield
F-1	3	Alpine Fir	2,000 to 8,000 in Oregon	A to G; Alaska to So. Oregon
F-2	3	White Fir	4,000 to 10,000	E to L; Columbia River to No. Mexico
F-5	—	Noble Fir	2,000 to 5,000	D to G; only in Oregon and Washington
F-6	1	Silver Fir	1,000 to 5,000	A to G; So. Alaska to Crater Lake, Ore.
F-7	—	Bristlecone Fir	2,200 to 5,000	J *spec.;* only in Santa Lucia Mts., Calif.
H-1	1,3	Western Hemlock	0 to 7,000	A to I; Alaska to Marin Co., Calif. (not in Siskiyous)
H-2	3	Mountain Hemlock	5,000 to 7,000 in Oregon	A to I; So. Alaska to Central California (sea level in the far north)
Hf-1	1,3	Douglas Fir	0 to 7,000	A to L; Canada to No. Mexico
Hf-2	1	Bigcone Spruce	1,500 to 6,000	K to L; So. and Lower California
J-2	1	Rocky Mountain Juniper	0 to 6,500 in Oregon	B to G; Canada to Mexico
J-3	3	Western Juniper	Mostly above 6,000 in California	D to K; Brit. Columbia to So. California
J-5	1	California Juniper	2,000 to 4,000	I to L *spec.;* Central California to No. Lower California
L-1	3	Western Larch	2,000 to 7,000	B to F; Brit. Columbia to No. Oregon
P-1	3	Sugar Pine	3,000 to 9,000 in Oregon	F to L; Oregon to Lower California
P-2	1,3	Western Yellow Pine	0 to 7,000 in Oregon	C to L; So. Brit. Columbia to No. Mexico
P-3	3	Jeffrey Pine	3,000 to 8,000	G to L; So. Oregon to Lower California
P-4	1,3	Lodgepole Pine	0 to 11,000	A to L; Alaska to Lower California
P-5	1,3	Western White Pine	0 to 10,000	B to K; Brit. Columbia to So. California
P-13	1	Bigcone Pine	2,500 to 6,000	I to L; north side of Mt. Diablo to Lower California
P-16	3	Singleleaf Pine	2,500 to 9,000	I to L; dry eastern slopes Sierra and Lower California
S-1	3	Engelmann Spruce	4,000 to 6,000 in Washington	A to G; Alaska to So. Oregon
S-3	3	Weeping Spruce	4,000 to 8,000	GH; S.W. Oregon and No. California
S-5	—	White Spruce	2,000 to 4,000	A; Alaska and east side of Rockies
To	1	California Nutmeg	0 to 6,000	I to K *spec.;* Lake and Mendocino to Kern Counties
Y	1,3	Western Yew	0 to 6,000	A to I; Alaska to Central California

ELEVATION ZONE 3

Conifers found at high elevations: *ABOVE* 5,000'
(Including those whose lower range limit is usually 5,000')

INDEX NO.	OTHER ELEV. ZONES	COMMON NAME	USUAL ELEV. RANGE, FT.	GEOGRAPHICAL DISTRIBUTION
C-2	2	Alaska Cedar	2,000 to 7,500 in Washington	A to G; So. Alaska to the Siskiyous
C-3	1,2	Incense Cedar	1,000 to 5,000 in Oregon	F to L; So. Alaska to Central California
C-4	1,2	Western Red Cedar	0 to 7,500	A to I; So. Alaska to No. California
F-1	2	Alpine Fir	2,000 to 8,000 in Oregon	A to G; Alaska to So. Oregon
F-2	2	White Fir	4,000 to 10,000	G to L; Columbia River to No. Mexico
F-4	—	California Red Fir	5,000 to 9,000 in Oregon	G to K; So. Oregon and No. California; ranges above F-2
H-1	1,2	Western Hemlock	0 to 7,000	A to I; Alaska to Marin Co., Calif. (not in Siskiyous)
H-2	2	Mountain Hemlock	5,000 to 7,000 in Oregon	A to I; So. Alaska to Central California; sea level in the north
Hf-1	1,2	Douglas Fir	0 to 7,000	A to L; Canada to No. Mexico
J-1	—	Dwarf Juniper	8,300 to 9,800 in California	A to J; sea level in Alaska; timber-line in California
J-3	2	Western Juniper	Mostly above 6,000 in California	D to K; Brit. Columbia to So. California
J-4	—	Utah Juniper	5,000 to 8,000	I to K; ranges eastward into Rocky Mts.
L-1	2	Western Larch	2,000 to 7,000	B to F; Brit. Columbia to No. Oregon
L-2	—	Alpine Larch	6,000 to 7,000	B to E; Canada as far south as Mt. Hood
P-1	2	Sugar Pine	3,000 to 9,000 in Oregon	F to L; Oregon to Lower California
P-2	1,2	Western Yellow Pine	0 to 7,000 in Oregon	C to L; So. Brit. Columbia to No. Mexico
P-3	2	Jeffrey Pine	3,000 to 8,000	G to L; So. Oregon to Lower California
P-4	1,2	Lodgepole Pine	0 to 11,000	A to L; Alaska to Lower California
P-5	1,2	Western White Pine	0 to 10,000	B to K; Brit. Columbia to So. California
P-10	—	Bristlecone Pine	7,000 to 11,000	I to K; So. Nevada and S.E. California at high elevations
P-11	—	White-bark Pine	7,000 to 11,000	C to K; Brit. Columbia to Mt. Whitney, near timberline
P-14	—	Limber Pine	5,000 to 12,000	B to L; Alaska to No. Mexico, at high elevations
P-15	—	Foxtail Pine	5,000 to 11,500	H to K *spec.*; in the Sierra near timberline
P-16	2	Singleleaf Pine	2,500 to 9,000	I to L; prefers dry eastern slope of Sierra and Lower California
P-17	2	Fourleaf Pine	4,000 to 8,000	K to L; So. and Lower California, in dry mountain regions
S-1	2	Engelmann Spruce	4,000 to 6,000 in Washington	A to G; Alaska to So. Oregon
S-3	2	Weeping Spruce	4,000 to 8,000	GH; S.W. Oregon and No. California
Se-1	—	Big Tree	5,000 to 8,000	IJ *spec.*; west slope of the Sierra
Y	1,2	Western Yew	0 to 6,000	A to I; Alaska to Central California

How to Use the Geographical Key

THE geographical key is a means of classifying the conifers according to their distribution along the Pacific Coast. There are two essential parts to this key: (1) a map on which lines like broad parallels of latitude have been drawn dividing the coast region into belts or districts and (2) a tabulation that groups the species occurring in each district.

For convenient reference each district on the map is marked with a letter (A, B, C, etc.). The district boundary lines are purposely made wide because the intent is to indicate these boundaries in a general rather than an exact way. Widths of the districts themselves were selected with a view to the simplest listings and the smallest number of districts consistent with a close marking of tree distributions. Some districts are purposely wider than those adjoining. For example, by making district J somewhat wider than district I and putting the northern boundary of J at about the upper limit of San Francisco Bay, it was possible to list rather accurately several species in fewer districts than otherwise would have been required.

This key enables the student to concentrate on the relatively small number of species occurring in the district under consideration. For example, if his interest for the time being is in trees that occur in the vicinity of Lake Tahoe (which is seen to be in district I), he will save much time in making identifications if he can turn at once to a listing in which appear *only* those species found in district I. As the list of species for each district is comparatively short, he can give attention to these exclusively and his decision as to identity of any particular tree will not be hampered and confused by the similar traits of trees that grow only in other districts.

GEOGRAPHICAL DISTRICTS

(PART I OF GEOGRAPHICAL KEY)

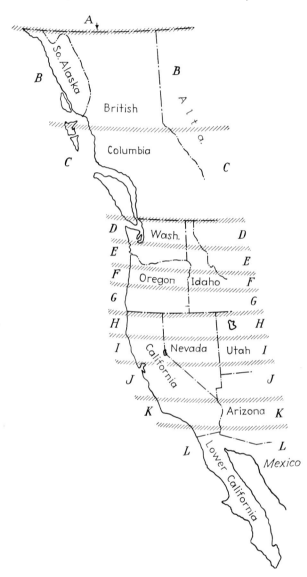

SPECIES GROUPED BY GEOGRAPHICAL DISTRICTS

District A

C-2	Alaska Cedar	J-1	Dwarf Juniper
C-4	Western Red Cedar	L-3	Tamarack
F-1	Alpine Fir	P-4	Lodgepole Pine
F-3	Grand Fir	S-1	Engelmann Spruce
F-6	Silver Fir	S-2	Sitka Spruce
H-1	Western Hemlock	S-4	Black Spruce
H-2	Mountain Hemlock	S-5	White Spruce
Hf-1	Douglas Fir	Y	Western Yew

District B

C-2	Alaska Cedar	J-2	Rocky Mountain Juniper
C-4	Western Red Cedar	L-1	Western Larch
F-1	Alpine Fir	L-2	Alpine Larch
F-3	Grand Fir	P-4	Lodgepole Pine
F-6	Silver Fir	P-5	Western White Pine
H-1	Western Hemlock	P-14	Limber Pine
H-2	Mountain Hemlock	S-1	Engelmann Spruce
Hf-1	Douglas Fir	S-2	Sitka Spruce
J-1	Dwarf Juniper	Y	Western Yew

District C

C-2	Alaska Cedar	L-1	Western Larch
C-4	Western Red Cedar	L-2	Alpine Larch
F-1	Alpine Fir	P-2	Western Yellow Pine
F-3	Grand Fir	P-4	Lodgepole Pine
F-6	Silver Fir	P-5	Western White Pine
H-1	Western Hemlock	P-11	White-bark Pine
H-2	Mountain Hemlock	P-14	Limber Pine
Hf-1	Douglas Fir	S-1	Engelmann Spruce
J-1	Dwarf Juniper	S-2	Sitka Spruce
J-2	Rocky Mountain Juniper	Y	Western Yew

District D

C-2	Alaska Cedar	J-3	Western Juniper
C-4	Western Red Cedar	L-1	Western Larch
F-1	Alpine Fir	L-2	Alpine Larch
F-3	Grand Fir	P-2	Western Yellow Pine
F-5	Noble Fir	P-4	Lodgepole Pine
F-6	Silver Fir	P-5	Western White Pine
H-1	Western Hemlock	P-11	White-bark Pine
H-2	Mountain Hemlock	P-14	Limber Pine
Hf-1	Douglas Fir	S-1	Engelmann Spruce
J-1	Dwarf Juniper	S-2	Sitka Spruce
J-2	Rocky Mountain Juniper	Y	Western Yew

District E

C-2	Alaska Cedar	J-3	Western Juniper
C-4	Western Red Cedar	L-1	Western Larch
F-1	Alpine Fir	L-2	Alpine Larch
F-3	Grand Fir	P-2	Western Yellow Pine
F-5	Noble Fir	P-4	Lodgepole Pine
F-6	Silver Fir	P-5	Western White Pine
H-1	Western Hemlock	P-11	White-bark Pine
H-2	Mountain Hemlock	P-14	Limber Pine
Hf-1	Douglas Fir	S-1	Engelmann Spruce
J-1	Dwarf Juniper	S-2	Sitka Spruce
J-2	Rocky Mountain Juniper	Y	Western Yew

District F

C-1	Port Orford Cedar	J-3	Western Juniper
C-2	Alaska Cedar	J-4	Utah Juniper
C-4	Western Red Cedar	L-1	Western Larch
F-1	Alpine Fir	P-1	Sugar Pine
F-3	Grand Fir	P-2	Western Yellow Pine
F-5	Noble Fir	P-4	Lodgepole Pine
F-6	Silver Fir	P-5	Western White Pine
H-1	Western Hemlock	P-11	White-bark Pine
H-2	Mountain Hemlock	P-14	Limber Pine
Hf-1	Douglas Fir	S-1	Engelmann Spruce
I	Incense Cedar	S-2	Sitka Spruce
J-1	Dwarf Juniper	Y	Western Yew
J-2	Rocky Mountain Juniper		

District G

C-1	Port Orford Cedar	J-3	Western Juniper
C-2	Alaska Cedar	J-4	Utah Juniper
C-4	Western Red Cedar	P-1	Sugar Pine
Cy-4	Macnab Cypress	P-2	Western Yellow Pine
F-1	Alpine Fir	P-3	Jeffrey Pine
F-2	White Fir	P-4	Lodgepole Pine
F-3	Grand Fir	P-5	Western White Pine
F-4	California Red Fir	P-6	Knobcone Pine
F-5	Noble Fir	P-11	White-bark Pine
F-6	Silver Fir	P-14	Limber Pine
H-1	Western Hemlock	S-1	Engelmann Spruce
H-2	Mountain Hemlock	S-2	Sitka Spruce
Hf-1	Douglas Fir	S-3	Weeping Spruce
I	Incense Cedar	Se-2	Redwood
J-1	Dwarf Juniper	Y	Western Yew
J-2	Rocky Mountain Juniper		

District H

C-1	Port Orford Cedar	P-1	Sugar Pine
C-2	Alaska Cedar	P-2	Western Yellow Pine
C-4	Western Red Cedar	P-3	Jeffrey Pine
Cy-4	Macnab Cypress	P-4	Lodgepole Pine
F-1	Alpine Fir	P-5	Western White Pine
F-2	White Fir	P-6	Knobcone Pine
F-3	Grand Fir	P-7	Digger Pine
F-4	California Red Fir	P-11	White-bark Pine
H-1	Western Hemlock	P-14	Limber Pine
H-2	Mountain Hemlock	P-15	Foxtail Pine
Hf-1	Douglas Fir	S-2	Sitka Spruce
I	Incense Cedar	S-3	Weeping Spruce
J-1	Dwarf Juniper	Se-2	Redwood
J-3	Western Juniper	Y	Western Yew
J-4	Utah Juniper		

District I

C-3	Incense Cedar	P-2	Western Yellow Pine
C-4	Western Red Cedar	P-3	Jeffrey Pine
Cy-3	Pygmy Cypress	P-4	Lodgepole Pine
Cy-4	Macnab Cypress	P-5	Western White Pine
Cy-7	Sargent Cypress	P-6	Knobcone Pine
F-1	Alpine Fir	P-7	Digger Pine
F-2	White Fir	P-9	Pricklecone Pine
F-3	Grand Fir	P-10	Bristlecone Pine
F-4	California Red Fir	P-11	White-bark Pine
H-1	Western Hemlock	P-13	Bigcone Pine
H-2	Mountain Hemlock	P-14	Limber Pine
Hf-1	Douglas Fir	P-15	Foxtail Pine
J-1	Dwarf Juniper	P-16	Singleleaf Pine
J-3	Western Juniper	S-2	Sitka Spruce
J-3	Western Juniper	Se-1	Big Tree
J-4	Utah Juniper	Se-2	Redwood
J-5	California Juniper	To	Calif. Nutmeg
P-1	Sugar Pine	Y	Western Yew

SPECIES GROUPED BY GEOGRAPHICAL DISTRICTS
(Continued)

District J

C-3	Incense Cedar	P-3	Jeffrey Pine
Cy-1	Monterey Cypress	P-4	Lodgepole Pine
Cy-2	Gowen Cypress	P-5	Western White Pine
Cy-6	Piute Cypress	P-6	Knobcone Pine
Cy-7	Sargent Cypress	P-7	Digger Pine
F-1	Alpine Fir	P-8	Monterey Pine
F-2	White Fir	P-9	Pricklecone Pine
F-4	California Red Fir	P-10	Bristlecone Pine
F-7	Bristlecone Fir	P-11	White-bark Pine
Hf-1	Douglas Fir	P-13	Bigcone Pine
J-1	Dwarf Juniper	P-14	Limber Pine
J-3	Western Juniper	P-15	Foxtail Pine
J-4	Utah Juniper	P-16	Singleleaf Pine
J-5	California Juniper	Se-1	Big Tree
P-1	Sugar Pine	Se-2	Redwood
P-2	Western Yellow Pine	To	California Nutmeg

District K

C-3	Incense Cedar	P-4	Lodgepole Pine
Cy-5	Tecate Cypress	P-5	Western White Pine
F-1	Alpine Fir	P-6	Knobcone Pine
F-2	White Fir	P-7	Digger Pine
F-4	California Red Fir	P-9	Pricklecone Pine
Hf-1	Douglas Fir	P-10	Bristlecone Pine
Hf-2	Bigcone Spruce	P-11	White-bark Pine
J-3	Western Juniper	P-13	Bigcone Pine
J-4	Utah Juniper	P-14	Limber Pine
J-5	California Juniper	P-15	Foxtail Pine
P-1	Sugar Pine	P-16	Singleleaf Pine
P-2	Western Yellow Pine	P-17	Fourleaf Pine
P-3	Jeffrey Pine	To	California Nutmeg

District L

C-3	Incense Cedar	P-3	Jeffrey Pine
Cy-5	Tecate Cypress	P-4	Lodgepole Pine
F-1	Alpine Fir	P-6	Knobcone Pine
F-2	White Fir	P-9	Pricklecone Pine
Hf-1	Douglas Fir	P-12	Torrey Pine
Hf-2	Bigcone Spruce	P-13	Bigcone Pine
K-5	California Juniper	P-14	Limber Pine
P-1	Sugar Pine	P-16	Singleleaf Pine
P-2	Western Yellow Pine	P-17	Fourleaf Pine

THE use of "cedar" in the common names of certain trees native to the Pacific Coast is unfortunate because it is misleading. It would be less confusing if "false cedar" had been used instead of "cedar." Danger of confusion can be avoided, however, if the student will remember that there are *no true cedars native to North America*. If this is kept in mind, the designations that include "cedar" will be recognized as merely popular names and will be treated as such.

Port Orford Cedar and Alaska Cedar, both of the genus *Chamaecyparis*, are closely related to the cypresses and share with them certain characteristics. Although the distributions are quite different, the general resemblance of the two groups is close enough to make it worth while to put emphasis on the finer distinctions between them. These are brought out clearly by selecting notable characteristics of the two groups and tabulating them for easy comparison. This is done in the following table.

ITEM FOR COMPARISON	CYPRESSES	FALSE CEDARS
Branchlet section.....................	Quadrangular	Flat
Branchlet arrangement...............	Irregular	In one plane
Leaf margins........................	Minutely toothed	Smooth
Cones mature.......................	In second season	In one season
Seeds under each fertile cone scale.....	15 to 20	4 or 5
Wings of seeds......................	Narrow, hard	Broad, gauzy
Seed leaves.........................	Three	Two

The four species of false cedar of which detailed descriptions follow are

U. S. Forest Service Photo

J. S. Forest Service Photo

Ore. Board of Forestry

(*Chamaecyparis Lawsoniana*)

Usual Occurrence:

Geographical range—F, G, H
Elevation range   —0 to 5,000′ (zones 1 and 2)
Foliage   —Scale-like

Leaves: About $\frac{1}{16}''$ long on lateral branchlets, $\frac{1}{8}$ to $\frac{1}{4}''$ on leaders; scale-like, in flat sprays, soft to the touch, in strong contrast with the prickly feel of cypress leaves. Bright green to pale yellow. Conspicuously glandular on the backs.

Cones: About $\frac{1}{3}''$ in diameter, berry-like, clustered on the upper branchlets in great profusion. One to four seeds under each cone-scale. Dark russet-brown, mature in one season. (Cones about same as Alaska Cypress —JL)

Bark: 6 to 8″ thick at base of mature tree, 3 to 4″ thick on smaller stems. Broken into long, loose, narrow ridges. Has two distinct layers. Brown with reddish tinge beneath.

Tree: In maturity 3 to 6′ × 100 to 175′ (max. 12 × 200′). Boles straight, crowns narrow with drooping branches. Mature trees have abruptly enlarged bases. Young trees have profusion of short, "feathery, weeping" branchlets with almost no clear trunk. At first all branches trend upward. As the tree grows older, they become horizontal and drooping, especially at the bottom of the crown. Old trees have clear boles for 80 to 100′.

Distribution: ★ Mainly in a Pacific Coast strip 225 miles long and rarely more than 40 miles wide. Coos Bay, Oregon, to Humboldt County, California. The heavy stand is on the coast, but some trees are found as far inland as the base of Mt. Shasta and at elevations up to 5,000′.

Other Names: Lawson's Cypress, White Cedar, Ginger Pine, Oregon Cedar.

In General: It is the chief species in the area between Coquille River, Oregon, and Point Gregory. Here there is a solid timber stand covering a 20- by 12-mile belt. One of the most valuable woods in the United States.

HH215; P41; Sgt77; Sh17; Su171

U.S. Forest Service Photo

Canadian Forest Service

U. S. Forest Service Photo

ALASKA CEDAR   C-2

(Chamaecyparis nootkatensis)

Usual Occurrence:

Geographical range—A to G inclusive

Elevation range　　—2,000 to 6,100′ in Oregon (zones 2 and 3)

Foliage　　　　　—Scale-like

Leaves: About ⅛″ long; longer (up to ¼″) with more elongated points on leaders. Scales overlap; twigs form an elk-horn pattern. The distinctively sharp and spreading points of the scales, which make the foliage harsh and prickly to the touch, are a feature that easily distinguishes this foliage from that of the Western Red Cedar.

Cones: Small (less than ½″ diameter) spherical, deep russet-brown with a very conspicuous whitish bloom. Four or six scales tipped with points. From two to four seeds under each fertile cone scale. Often covered with conspicuous resin glands.

Bark: Ashy-brown, about ⅝″ thick. Clear reddish brown inside. Large, thin, loose scales.

Tree: In maturity 3 to 4′ × 80 to 90′ or more. Open, narrowly conical crown;★ as a whole; has a weeping appearance due to drooping branches. Branches few and far distant from one another. Exceedingly slender. whip-like leader too weak at its tip to stand erect, so it bends over gracefully, Branches sometimes extend close to the ground. Trunks always more or less fluted and infolded at the base. At high elevations sometimes a low shrub.

Distribution: From southern Alaska to the Siskiyous of southern Oregon. In Washington found between elevation 2,000 and 7,500′. Sudworth gives elevation range as follows:

Alaska. . . . . 0 to 2,000 or 3,000′ (timberline)

British Columbia. . 0 to 5,000′ (latter figure in southern British Columbia)

Washington. . . . . . . 2,000 to 7,500′ (latter on Mt. Rainier)

Oregon. . . . . 2,500 to 6,100′ (latter on Mt. Hood)

Other Names: Yellow Cedar, Yellow Cypress, Alaska Cypress, Sitka Cypress, Nootka Cypress, Canoe Cedar.

In General: Might be mistaken for Western Red Cedar, on casual observation; there is distinction in the "weeping" appearance given by the drooping branches of the Alaska Cedar. For more exact comparisons a sharp distinction lies in the fact that wood of the Alaska Cedar is a sulphur-yellow★ and is heavier by 10 to 12 lb. per cubic foot than Western Red Cedar.

Can70; HH216; P65; Sgt76; Su168

C-3

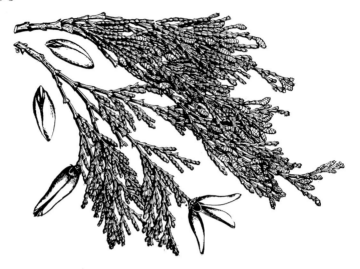

U. S. Forest Service Photos

INCENSE CEDAR   C-3

(Libocedrus decurrens)

Usual Occurrence:
Geographical range—F to L inclusive
Elevation range   —1,000 to 5,000′ in Oregon (zones 1, 2, and 3)
Foliage   —Scale-like

Leaves: Scales overlap, are keeled and glandular on the back, and have sharp tips.   Length is ⅛″ on lateral branchlets to nearly ½″ on leaders. The scales are longer than in Western Red Cedar; twigs are not so bushy, having an almost snaky pattern.   Foliage as a whole is yellow-green, gives off pungent odor when crushed.

Cones: Small, elongated cones (¾ to 1″ long) more like a flower, each with two seed leaves★ (four little seeds, ⅓ to ½″ long, two each side of the partition—Sh).   Very different from other cedar cones; pungently odorous. Partially opened cone has the appearance of a duck's bill.

Bark: Cinnamon-brown, 2 to 3″ thick at the base (some authorities give thicknesses of 6 to 8″); can be peeled off in long strips; is highly resistant to fire.

Tree: In maturity 2 to 4′ × 75 × 100′.   Mature trees have rapidly tapering trunks and widely buttressed bases.   "Slender branches erect at the top of the tree, below sweeping downward in bold curves, forming a narrow open feathery crown becoming in old age irregular in outline by the greater development of a few ultimately upright branches forming secondary stems."—Sgt

Distribution: From southern slope of Mt. Hood, Oregon, through California and western Nevada to Lower California.   Common in Coast Range and Sierra.   In Oregon 1,000 to 5,000′.   Western side of Sierra Nevada 2,500 to 7,000′; most abundant between 5,000 to 7,000′.   In southern California 3,000 to 8,000 or 9,000′ (Ch).   California has by far the largest number of these trees.

Other Names: White Cedar, Red Cedar, Post Cedar, Bastard Cedar, Juniper.

HH199; Ch81; P65; Sh12; Sgt65; Su148

U. S. Forest Service Photo

Usual Occurrence:

Geographical range—A to I inclusive

Elevation range   —0 to 7,500' (zones 1, 2, and 3)

Foliage   —Scale-like

Leaves: Scale-like, overlapping, frequently $\frac{1}{4}''$ long, ★ often conspicuously glandular on the back. Branchlets have flat "elk-horn" or fern-like pattern. Flat, lace-like, yellow-green side sprays hang from the branches like lines of fringe. Spicy odor. Mostly persist 2 to 5 years. Foliage is darker green on top and lighter underneath than in other cedars.

Cones: $\frac{1}{4}$ to 2" long, like miniature buds resembling a Dutchman's pipe. Have about six seed-bearing scales, each covering two or three very small seeds; wings, about $\frac{1}{4}''$ long, on both sides of seed.

Bark: ★Thin, from $\frac{5}{8}$ to $\frac{7}{8}''$ thick. Frequently a bright cinnamon-brown, often weathered to gray-brown. Bark is shreddy and readily inflammable.

Tree: In maturity $3\frac{1}{2}$ to $8' \times 150$ to $175'$ (max. 10 to $16' \times 200'$). Entire bole has conical form due to rapid taper. ★Mature trees have conspicuous basal buttresses which are fluted. A notable feature of the tree is the frequent occurrence of two leaders which combine in forming a dense crown. On young trees limbs curve upward; later there is a characteristic downward swing of long branches with an upward sweep at the ends.

Distribution: Southern Alaska to Mendocino County, California, east to Idaho and Montana. Prefers wet or even swampy locations, though not necessarily at low elevations. Elevation range is from sea level to 7,500' (on rim of Crater Lake). Usually stunted when found in dry locations.

Other Names: Cedar, Western Cedar, Canoe Cedar, Red Cedar, Giant Cedar, Arborvitae, Giant Arborvitae, Shinglewood, *Thuja gigantea*.

In General: Largest of the false cedars. Indians peel off strips of bark 20 or even 30' long from young trees for use in basketmaking. Wood is strongly aromatic and is the lightest of all the conifers; 1 cu. ft. weighs only 24 lb., less than half the weight of the heavier woods.

Can65; HH205; P38; Sgt68; Sh13; Su153

SEVEN species of cypress are native to the Pacific Coast north of Mexico. All seven are found in California, and only one grows naturally outside that state. This one, a species found in the foothills of mountains in the northern part of the state, merely extends its range, with fine disregard for the boundaries set up by man, into southern Oregon. Thus, cypresses of the Pacific Coast come close to being exclusively "native sons" of one state.

A tabulation of fundamental differences between false cedars and cypresses is given in the introduction to the former.

Data about the cypresses are arranged in this manual in a form different from that used for all other tree groups. This is because all seven species of cypress are much alike when trees of similar age and form are compared. However, it happens that unlike most other genera (groups) such as juniper, spruce, etc., the genus cypress consists of species whose native habitats are limited to well-defined areas (arboreal islands). Hence geographical location becomes a convenient and most effective aid to identification. Five of the seven species are found in areas of a very few miles in extent. These areas are indicated and identified on the accompanying outline map of California. The other two have wider ranges; but the distributions overlap only slightly, so here again identification can be aided effectively by a knowledge of geographical range.

None of the cypresses occur in extensive groves; they tend, rather, to isolated groups. In the two species that have far-ranging distribution these isolated groups may be widely separated; in the other five species, confined to relatively small arboreal islands, the individual trees may be limited to a few adjacent groups.

All the cypresses have scale-like foliage; all have nut-like cones much the same in size and general appearance; and all but two are limited to elevation zone 1.

The following paragraphs, based on classifications made by several botanists, and with special acknowledgment to Dr. C. B. Wolf of Rancho Santa Ana Botanic Gardens, summarize what

GEOGRAPHICAL DISTRICTS

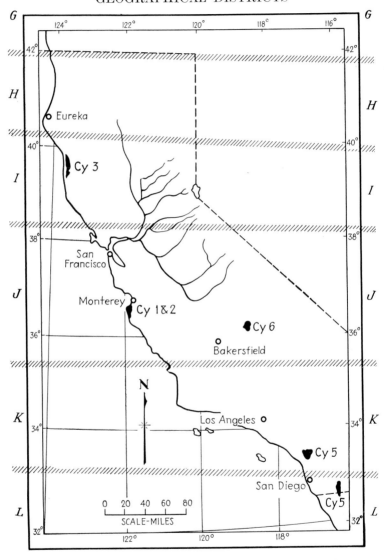

little there is to be said about distinguishing traits of the seven species. Geographical distribution is placed first in each paragraph and should be considered in connection with the accompanying outline map on which the geographical distributions of five of the seven species are indicated.

The seven species of cypress described in this manual are:

Monterey Cypress.................................. Cy-1
    (*Cupressus macrocarpa*)
Gowen Cypress.................................... Cy-2
    (*Cupressus Goveniana*)
Pygmy Cypress.................................... Cy-3
    (*Cupressus pygmaea*)
Macnab Cypress................................... Cy-4
    (*Cupressus Macnabiana*)
    Also *var:*
    Baker's Cypress
      (*Cupressus Bakeri*)
Tecate Cypress................................... Cy-5
    (*Cupressus Forbesii*)
Piute Cypress.................................... Cy-6
    (*Cupressus nevadensis*)
Sargent Cypress.................................. Cy-7
    (*Cupressus Sargentii*)
    Also *var:*
    Dutton's Cypress
      (*Cupressus Sargentii*, var. *Duttoni*)

Cy-1

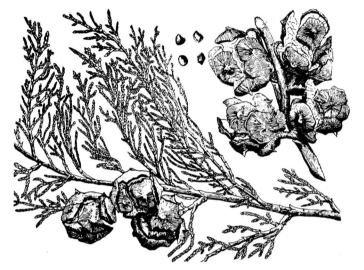

W. L. Huber Photo

· 44 ·

Cy-1   Monterey Cypress   (*Cupressus macrocarpa*)

The Monterey Cypress is found close to the shoreline on rocky headlands overlooking the ocean on the north and on the south sides of Carmel Bay. This bay, on the west side of the Monterey Peninsula, borders the shaded area marked Cy-1 and 2 on the Cypress geographical range map (district J, not above elevation 100'). Typical specimens are found along the 17-mile drive that skirts the shore on the westerly side of the peninsula.

In maturity 18 to 20″ × 40 to 50', specimens very rarely exceed 60' in height. Further development made as the trees age takes the form of long massive limbs which finally attain the height of the leader and spread out into a wide, umbrella-shaped crown. Sea winds may cause enormously developed limbs to sprawl along the ground, grotesquely bent and gnarled. Violent swaying of the branches sometimes produces curious enlargements at the bases of the branches, obviously serving as braces.

This species is extensively cultivated for windbreaks because of the rapid growth of young trees. The latter have a form entirely different from that typical of maturity; *i.e.*, young trunks are sharply conical and have crowns of rigidly straight branches extending upward in a wide pointed pyramid that starts from the ground.

Drawings of cones and foliage of the Monterey Cypress are included in the manual not because they have any peculiar traits that will be used in identifying this particular species but because the student will need to visualize typical cones and foliage of the cypresses generally. As the seven species are very much alike in these respects, Monterey Cypress will serve as well as any other.

Cy-2   Gowen Cypress   (*Cupressus Goveniana*)

The Gowen Cypress is a shrub or low tree with the typical cypress cones, growing farther back from the immediate shore-line than the Monterey Cypress. The two trees are found in the same general area, *i.e.*, the shaded area marked Cy-1 and 2 on the geographical range map (district J, elevation 200 to 500').

Cy-3   **Pygmy Cypress**   (*Cupressus pygmaea*)

The Pygmy Cypress, varying in size from a dwarf to a tall tree, has a geographical range restricted to a narrow coastal plain along the ocean shore in Mendocino County. This location is marked Cy-3 on the geographical range map (district I, elevation range 200 to 1,000').

Cy-4   **Macnab Cypress**   (*Cupressus Macnabiana*)

The distribution of the Macnab Cypress (sometimes called "White Cedar" or "Shasta Cypress") is not indicated on the map because this is one of the two far-ranging species. It occurs along the dry Sierra foothills from Yuba County to the Oregon line and slightly beyond. Also it extends from its northern limits some distance to the south along the Coast Range Mountains on the western side of the Sacramento Valley, thus giving the geographical distribution a shape somewhat like a horseshoe curving around the north end of the Sacramento Valley (districts G, H, and I; elevation range 1,000 to 2,000'). Distinguishing traits of this species are a conspicuous resin gland on the back or outer side of each scale (leaf) and long, generally incurving horns on the cone scales. (See Sargent Cypress for comparison of traits of these two species.)

A variation of Sargent Cypress, known as "Baker's Cypress" (*Cupressus Bakeri*), is found in the Modoc lava beds of Siskiyou County at an altitude of about 4,000'. It is also reported on Steve's Peak in southern Oregon as high as 6,000'. This variety has short horns on the cone scales: in recent years it has been regarded by some authorities as a distinct species.

Cy-5   **Tecate Cypress**   (*Cupressus Forbesii*)

The Tecate Cypress is known only in two areas, each quite limited, in the mountains of San Diego and Orange Counties. These locations are indicated by the two shaded areas marked Cy-5 on the geographical range map (districts K and L, elevation range 700 to 4,200').

This species is characterized by its very smooth reddish bark—a trait that is the more distinctive because all other cypresses of California have scaly, fissured, or fibrous bark.

Cy-6   **Piute Cypress**   (*Cupressus nevadensis*)

Piute Cypress is known only on the slopes of Piute Mountain in Kern County, marked by the shaded area Cy-6 on the geographical range map (district J, at an elevation of 4,000'). This species has conspicuous resin glands on the scales and nearly straight horns on the cone scales.

Cy-7   **Sargent Cypress**   (*Cupressus Sargentii*)

Sargent Cypress, the second of the two far-ranging species whose distribution is not indicated on the map, occurs in widely separated thickets and groves scattered through the Coast Range Mountains all the way from San Luis Obispo County on the south to Mendocino and Lake Counties on the north (districts I and J, elevation range 200 to 2,500'). Its elevation range usually is about 1,000', and it has a decided preference for locations where it can find root in the soft rock formation known as "serpentine."

In mountains of the Coast Range north of San Francisco, distributions of Macnab and the Sargent Cypress overlap. In this region the student will need to examine the foliage and cones to be sure of making a distinction between the two species. Leaves of the Macnab Cypress have open resin glands, and the resin, after exuding and hardening, forms little globules on the backs of the leaves, thus emphasizing the presence of the glands. These are not large (about the size of the head of a pin), but they age a frosty-white and hence become quite conspicuous against the green background. Cones of the Macnab Cypress have horns that tend to curve inward. In contrast to these traits, scales (leaves) of Sargent Cypress have no visible resin glands, and cones are nearly smooth.

Dr. Wolf lists a variety of this species (*Cupressus Sargentii*, var. *Dutttoni*) occurring at elevation 3,000' on Cedar Mountain in Alameda County.

S EVEN species of fir are native to the Pacific Coast.   These all
have certain characteristics in common.   In fact, "a fir may be
identified as such long before its particular species is determined."

Fir crowns are characteristically conical, often spire-like with
dense, heavily foliaged branches.   Usually the crowns are very
dark green, and the branches all point upward.   The heads are
thus sharply defined and arrow-like, which makes them stand
out among other trees.   The erect position of the cones is unique
and distinctive of all firs.   Cones mature in one season.   There
are two seeds under each cone scale.   The cones of all the firs
fall to pieces after maturity while the stem is still attached to
the tree.   Thus one does not find fir cones beneath the trees as
is the case with many other conifers.

The trunk bark, before it is broken and furrowed by age, is
marked by many blister-like resin pockets formed within and
just beneath the smooth surface.   This characteristic has given
them the popular name of "balsams" because of the liquid resin
obtained from the pockets which is used for medicinal purposes.

The most certain means of distinguishing the several species of
firs is by their cones.   But there are no cones on the trees during
a considerable portion of the year, and every other year they
bear sparsely if at all.   Trunk and bark as a means of identification will serve well in certain species, not so well in others, and
hardly ever in the case of very young trees.   Hence needles
become the most important means of identification; and in the
firs even more than in other conifers, careful study of needle
characteristics is well worth while.

On all firs needles are attached singly to the branchlets, but
needle traits vary greatly in different locations on the same tree.
It is important to note the very dissimilar form, habit, and
character of needles in different parts of the tree.   Leaves from
the middle branches are sometimes different in form from those
of either the upper or the lower branches.

Needles on the lower branches are mostly flat (in one species
triangular), rounded or blunt at the ends (one species is prickly
pointed), and they grow more or less distinctly from two opposite
sides of the branchlets.

In several species of fir the needles are attached on all sides of the branchlets but despite this manage to twist in their bases so that they appear to come from opposite sides of the branchlets only, thus giving the characteristic "flat spray" effect.

Needles on the extreme upper branches are crowded and curved toward the upper sides of the horizontal twigs, giving a brush-like appearance. It is often found that needles near the top of the crown are more sharply pointed than those lower down.

Male and female flowers of firs are borne on branchlets of the previous year's growth in different parts of the same tree. Female flowers, producing cones (and seeds), stand erect on uppermost parts of the crown. Male flowers, bearing pollen, hang below the lower side of branches at lower levels.

The seven species of fir of which detailed descriptions follow are

Alpine Fir.. F-1
  (*Abies lasiocarpa*)
White Fir... F-2
  (*Abies concolor*)
Grand Fir... F-3
  (*Abies grandis*)
Red Fir... F-4
  (*Abies magnifica*)
Noble Fir... F-5
  (*Abies nobilis*)
Silver Fir.. F-6
  (*Abies amabilis*)
Bristlecone Fir................................... F-7
  (*Abies venusta*)

U. S. Forest Service Photo

(*Abies lasiocarpa*)

Usual Occurrence:
  Geographical range—A to L inclusive
  Elevation range   —2,000 to 7,900′ in Oregon (zones 2 and 3)
  Foliage   —Needles, attached singly
  Needles: 1 to 1¾″ long on lower branches, not more than ½″ on upper branches; have conspicuous midrib.   Tips of the needles are notched except on some of the top branches.   Distinctively massed, and pointing upward on the upper sides of the branchlets, those below and on the sides being twisted so as to join those above.   ★This dense crowding is very characteristic.   Foliage deep blue-green.   "Cutting across a needle of alpine fir with a sharp knife will show two resin ducts, plainly visible to the naked eye, having the appearance of *two little eyes*.   These ducts, as visible in this way, are not found in the needles of any of the other true firs."—JL
  Cones: When mature, and before swelling and beginning to break up, are 2¼ to 4″ long and about 1¼ to 1½″ in diameter.   They are deep purple, becoming lighter by the time the scales fall.
  Bark: Thin.   At most about 1¼″ thick.   Hard and flinty.   Unbroken, smooth parts of bark on mature trees are ashy-gray to chalky-white.
  Tree: The distinguishing feature of this species is the long, narrowly conical crown terminating in a conspicuous, spire-like point.   This spear-like head can be recognized at a great distance.   In favorable locations trees attain a size of 14 to 24″ × 60 to 90′ (2 to 4′ × 100′, occasionally 175′—Sgt), although in high, exposed locations it may be only 3 to 4′ high with long lower branches on the ground.   Crown usually extends to the ground, even in old trees.   Lower branches droop.
  Distribution: Alaska, British Columbia, Washington, Oregon, Idaho, Wyoming, Utah, and Arizona at or close to timberline.   (Not a native of California.)   Prefers locations where snowfalls are deep.   Endures rigorous climate, and hence goes farther north than any other fir of this region.   Elevation range:

  Alaska. . . . . 0 to 3,000′
  British Colombia. . . . . 2,000 to 7,000′
  Washington and Oregon. . . . . 2,000 to 7,900′

  Other Names: Mountain Fir, Rocky Mountain Fir, White Fir, Balsam, White Balsam, Western Balsam Fir, Caribou Fir, Mountain Balsam, Oregon Balsam-tree.
  In General: Because of the close similarity between Alpine Fir and Silver Fir (F-6) there is need for special care in distinguishing these two trees.   John A. Lee suggests the following:
  1. "On the upper sides of Alpine Fir needles there is a whitish color (caused by stomata) which does not appear on the upper surface of Silver Fir needles.
  2. "Silver Fir has and Alpine Fir does not have needles twisted at their bases."

HH179; Can54; Sgt53; Su107

U. S. Forest Service Photos

(Abies concolor)

Usual Occurrence:

Geographical range—G to L inclusive

Elevation range   —4,000 to 10,000′ in South (zones 2 and 3)

Foliage   —Needles, attached singly

Needles: In flat rows, 1 to 2″ long, fragrant.   Full and plump on the upper side.   On the lower branches they are 1⅓ to 3″ long.   Needles of the upper crown are strong, curving, or sickle-shaped, 1 to 1⅓″ long.   Tips rounded and blunt.   Unlike the Red Fir, with which it associates in California, White Fir needles have a distinctly *separate* appearance.   "To distinguish between *concolor* and *grandis* (F-3)," John A. Lee says, "note that *concolor* needles have a whitish appearance (caused by stomata) on *both* upper and lower sides while needles of the *grandis* have no stomata on their upper sides."

Cones: Stand upright on upper branches, 3 to 4″ long.   Bracts attached to backs of cone scales are narrow, oblong, and squarish at the outer end, which has a small point extending from its center.

Bark: Ash-gray bark 4 to 6½″ thick is conspicuously rough with great, deep furrows and ridges—very hard and horny.   Frequently rougher than that of any tree that it resembles.

Tree: 4 to 5′ × 140 to 180 or 200′.   Branches of young trees grow in whorls.

Distribution: From Columbia River southward to northern Mexico— mainly on west slope of the Sierra.   Never in pure stands but often forms three-fourths of a stand.   As low as elevation 1,300′ in Feather River canyon but ordinarily a high-altitude tree, ranging from 4,000 or 5,000′ up to about 10,000′ in the South.

Other Names: Balsam Fir, Silver Fir, Balsam, California White Fir.

In General: In appearance something like Douglas Fir, but usually not found below 3,000 to 4,000′ elevation.   There is great variation in length, form, and thickness of needles of this species.

HH172; Ch69; P66; Sgt55; Sh9; Su116

U. S. Forest Service Photos

GRAND FIR   F-3
(*Abies grandis*)

Usual Occurrence:
>Geographical range—A to I inclusive
>Elevation range   —0 to 3,000′ in Oregon (zone 1)
>Foliage   —Needles, attached singly

Needles: 1 to 2½″ long. On lower branches, two-ranked and flat, grooved and blunt, with *notched* tips. The foliage is thin in appearance because of the characteristic spreading. On upper branches dense and shorter (1 to 1¼″), tending to turn upward, brush-like, as in the Noble Fir, F-5. All needles conspicuously white on their under surfaces. "In young trees each section of a spray," says John A. Lee, "shows an elliptical outline of needle arrangement because needle lengths decrease toward each end of the section. This test will suffice for young trees at all elevations but is not applicable to higher branches of mature trees or even to the lower branches of mature trees at the higher elevations. In these latter cases the needles usually are more than two-ranked."

Cones: 2 to 4″ long. 1½ to 2″ diameter. Axis of cone from previous year often remains upright on branch. No other cone has this blunt, rounded tip and relatively great breadth of scales. Bracts do not protrude, adhere to backs of cone scales, are squarish, and have a small point at center of outer end.

Bark: Conspicuously whitish, smooth bark earns for this tree the name "White" Fir. Rather thick bark, for a fir, often cut by narrow furrows into hard, sharp, horny ridges.

Tree: Straight trunk. In maturity 3 to 4′ × 150 to 250′. Tops narrow and pointed, crown extending nearly to the ground in open stands; in forests, covers about half the stem. "All of the branches except the topmost have a distinct downward and upward swing." That is, they tend to droop slightly and then turn up at the ends.

Distribution: British Columbia to Sonoma County, California, north of Fort Ross, east to Montana. Decidedly a lowland tree. Best growth in moist valleys and lower slopes. (In Oregon only fir found at sea level; not found in Oregon above 3,000′ and at this height only in gullies and moist places.) In California, according to Sargent, rarely more than 10 miles inland or higher than elevation 1,500′.

Other Names: Stinking Fir, Lowland Fir, White Fir, Western White Fir, Oregon White Fir, Silver Fir, Western Balsam, Balsam Fir, Lowland White Fir, Larch, Giant Fir, Yellow Fir, Rough-barked Fir.

In General: Wood is very knotty and decays quickly—little used for lumber. Ordinarily this tree may be identified by the disagreeable odor of the wood; hence "Stinking Fir." A very stately tree when fully matured.

HH177; Can55; P51; Sgt54; Su111

U. S. Forest Service Photo

(*Abies magnifica*)

Usual Occurrence:
Geographical range—G to K inclusive
Elevation range   —5,000 to 9,000′ in Oregon (zone 3)
Foliage   —Needles, attached singly

Needles: Usually ¾ to 1¼″ long on lower branches.   Mature needles are a deep green—new foliage is silvery, four-angled, plump, and full.   Longer and flatter on lower branches, shorter and closer set near the top.   Branchlets up high, seen from below, have the appearance of having a uniform, *round* cross-section.   To distinguish between Red Fir and Noble Fir, see notes under latter, F-5.

Cones: Upright, 5 to 6″ high (sometimes 8 to 9″ long × 2¾ to 3½″ in diameter).

Bark: ★Dark brown, sometimes almost black in old trees, 2 to 3″ thick (Sargent says 4 to 6″), irregularly divided by diagonal furrows which give a peculiar zigzag trend to the ridges.   No other tree in the habitat of this fir has anything like this bark.

Tree: In maturity 3 to 4′ × 125 to 150′ (max. 10 × 200′).   On steep slopes often bend downhill, the effect of heavy snows which yearly bend seedlings to the ground and from which the tree sometimes never wholly recovers.   Crown often extends all the way to the ground.   The largest of all American firs.

Distribution: Nominally southern Oregon and northern California, though some are found in the southern Sierra.   (5,000 to 9,000′ in Oregon.)   A tree of high elevation, often extending up to timberline in its range.

Other Names: A very similar tree, Shasta Red Fir (*Abies magnifica shastensis*), has the same range and the same needle characteristics and apparently is the same in all particulars *except* that distinction can be made if *cones* can be examined.   The cones of the Shasta Red Fir have extended, drooping bracts, as in the Noble Fir, whereas the Red Fir has no protruding bracts.

To distinguish Shasta Red Fir and the Red Fir from the Noble Fir, John A. Lee says: "Look for grooves on the needles.   Needles of the *nobilis* have a clearly defined groove extending along the middle of the upper surface.   This groove is not present in needles of the *magnifica* or *shastensis*, although all three needles are alike in all other respects.   The Shasta Red Fir and the Noble Fir have cones so similar that it is better to make distinction by this needle test."

In General: Resembles the White Fir but found at higher elevations.   Takes its name (Red Fir) from the bark.

This is the "Silver Tip" or "Silver Fir" of Christmas-tree trade which rapidly has attained great popularity in recent years.   The young trees are almost perfectly symmetrical in form and have upturned, sturdy branches and limbs that can carry a heavy Christmas load without drooping.

HH167; Ch72; P66; Sgt58; Sh10; Su132

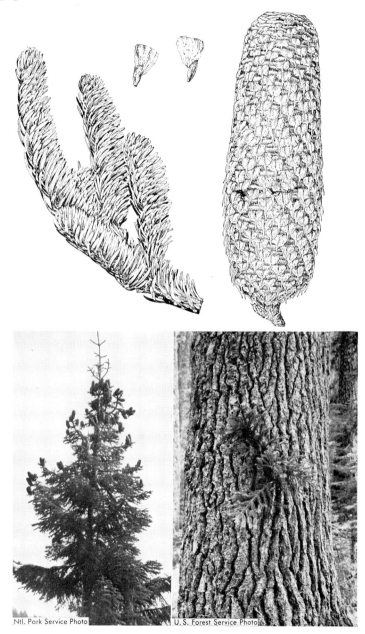

Ntl. Park Service Photo

U. S. Forest Service Photo

(*Abies nobilis*)

Usual Occurrence:

        Geographical range—D, E, F, G

        Elevation range   —2,000 to 5,000′ (zone 2)

        Foliage   —Needles, attached singly

Needles: On exposed branches curved to upper side giving very compact brush-like appearance with twig constituting under side or base of brush. Four-angled, pointed, and about $\frac{3}{4}''$ long. On sheltered branchlets or juvenile specimens needles are flat, usually notched at ends, and about 1 to $1\frac{1}{2}''$ long.

Cones: Of compact and solid appearance, 4 to 6″ long, 2 to 3″ in diameter, cylindrical, flat topped, standing erect on branches, and usually massed near top of tree.   ★Frequent bracts; irregularly notched, with long tapering point protruding and hanging downward.

Bark: 1 to 2″ thick divided into flat, narrow ridges.

Tree: In maturity 3 to 6′ × 140 to 200′.   In dense stands, clear bole for 100′ or more.   Short, stiff-looking branches stand out straight from the stem.   Lower branches often droop.

Distribution: Only in Oregon and Washington—southward nearly to the Siskiyous.   Elevation range usually 2,000 to 5,000′.

Other Names: Red Fir, Balsam, Balsam Fir.   Improperly but deliberately called "larch" by lumbermen to avoid a prejudice against fir lumber. Noble Fir is in no way related to larch.

In General: The Noble Fir and its near relatives, the Red Fir and the Shasta Red Fir, differ from all the other true firs in having the same or very nearly the same color on the under side of the needles as on the upper side. (John A. Lee says that he never knew this test to fail to be distinctive of these varieties.)   The color is a solid, rather light green, usually a shade lighter on the under side.   All other firs, on the other hand, have a *decidedly whitish* appearance on the under side of their needles because of the presence of many stomata.

For distinctions between Noble Fir, Red Fir, and Shasta Red Fir, see F-4.

HH171; P49; Sgt57; Su128

F-6

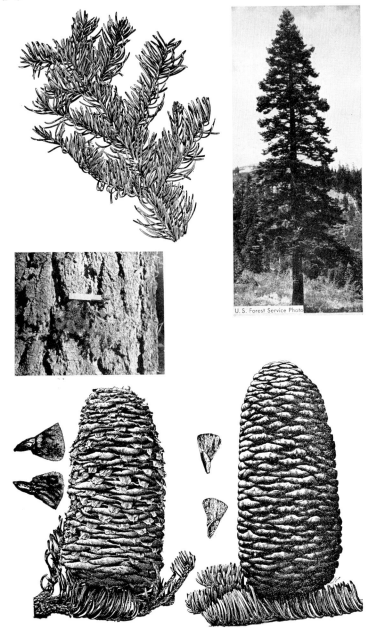

U. S. Forest Service Photo

(Abies amabilis)

Usual Occurrence:

    Geographical range—A to G inclusive

    Elevation range   —1,000 to 5,000′ (zones 1 and 2)

    Foliage   —Needles, attached singly

Needles: Usually $\frac{3}{4}$ to $1\frac{1}{4}''$ long. On lower branches flat and sharply grooved on upper side, white lined below, usually (though not always) notched at the ends. Appear massed above branchlets due to twist in stems. Branches on upper crown have shorter and stouter leaves about $\frac{3}{4}''$ long, standing erect in dense masses. Needles on leaders are keenly pointed. [Needle traits that distinguish this tree from Alpine Fir (F-1) are described in notes on F-1.]

Cones: Dark purple cones $3\frac{1}{2}$ to $6''$ long $\times$ $2\frac{1}{4}$ to $2\frac{1}{2}''$ thick. Bracts adhering to backs of cone scales are rounded at their outer ends, narrowing to a long, thin point.   (Cones are larger than those of the Alpine Fir.—JL)

Bark: Thin, smooth, ashy-gray bark with chalky-white areas, even on trees up to 150 years old.

Tree: In maturity 3 to $5' \times 150$ to 180 or $200'$. All branches except uppermost droop markedly, those at the bottom of the crown most. In close, dense stands it is clear of branches for 50 to $100'$.

Distribution: From southern Alaska south to Crater Lake. Elevation 1,000 to 5,000′.

Other Names: White Fir or Silver Fir because of the smooth white bark. Lovely Fir, Red Fir, Red Silver Fir, Alpine Fir, Larch.

HH165; Can57; P66; Sgt56; Su125

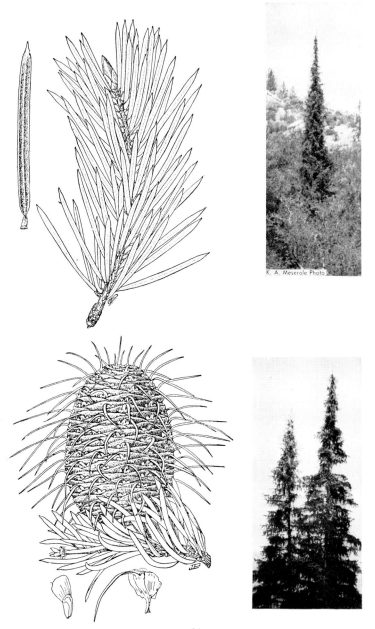

(Abies venusta)

Usual Occurrence:

Geographical range—J

Elevation range   —2,200 to 5,000' (zone 2)

Foliage   —Needles, attached singly

Needles: Usually 1¾ to 2″ long, thin, flat, rigid, keenly pointed, lustrous needles. Under sides are white lined. Flat sprays on lower branches; upward crowding forces needles into brush-like form on upper branches.

Cones: About 2¾ to 3½″ long and at maturity have a faint purplish color. ★Egg-shaped, bristling with slender needle-like bracts.

Bark: At base of tree ½ to ¾″ thick, light reddish brown, slightly and irregularly broken into thick scabs.

Tree: Mature trees 20 to 30″ × 60 to 100'. ★Sharply pointed, spire-like crowns are so distinctive as to make the tree stand out so it can be recognized from among others while the observer is more than a mile away. All branches droop conspicuously.

Distribution: *Spec.* Scattered patches grow in Monterey County at the heads of canyons and on seaward slopes of Santa Lucia Mountains. Elevation 2,200 to 5,000'.

Other Names: Santa Lucia Fir *(Abies bracteata).*

In General: The rarest of California firs, unique in practically all its characteristics. "The most curious fir tree in the world."

HH182; Sgt60; Sh11; Su121

FOUR species of hemlock are native to the United States and Canada. Two of these inhabit the eastern United States and adjacent Canadian provinces, and two, Western Hemlock and Mountain Hemlock, are found in Pacific forests.

Typical of the hemlocks are the slender terminal sprays that trail downward gracefully and the slender leaders that droop and nod conspicuously.

The characteristically rough, hard, bark, ridged and furrowed, contains tannin which gives it an astringent taste. When the bark is broken, the color is a clear chocolate-red. Hemlock is important both for saw timber and tanbark.

Hemlock needles are peculiar in having a single resin duct located in the center of the cross-section near the lower surface.

The two species of hemlock of which detailed descriptions follow are:

Canadian Forest Service

1 inch

Canadian Forest Service

Usual Occurrence:
Geographical range—A to I inclusive
Elevation range   —0 to 7,000′ (zones 1, 2, and 3)
Foliage   —Needles, attached singly

Needles: Attached singly, flat, grooved above; have blunt, rounded ends, $\frac{1}{4}$ to 1″ long. Appear to grow mainly from opposite sides of the branchlets. Mostly persistent 4 to 7 years.

Cones:★ Small, abundant; have few scales, which are longer than they are broad and are coated on the upper surface with fine down. Cones are pendulous from tips of branchlets, $\frac{3}{4}$ to $1\frac{1}{4}$″ long. Two seeds, $\frac{1}{8}$″ long, under each cone scale, have relatively large wings. Most of the cones drop during the winter.

Bark: Smooth, russet-brown, tinged with red. In mature trees 1 to $1\frac{1}{2}$″ thick, deeply furrowed. The ridges are wide, flat, and irregularly connected with one another by narrower cross ridges.

Tree: In maturity 2 to 5′ × 125 to 160′ (max. 10 × 200′). Small branches pendulous. A tree of graceful appearance because of the fine, lacy foliage. One of the most beautiful of all the conifers. "It always may be identified by ★the drooping tips of the branches, especially the gracefully drooping leader." The base of the trunk often is much swollen or thickened. Largest of the American hemlocks.

Distribution: From Alaska as far south as Marin County, California, eastward into Idaho. Not found in the Siskiyous—prefers wet locations, sea level to 7,000′. Rapid growth on cut-over land makes it valuable for pulpwood.

Other Names: Lowland Hemlock, Hemlock Spruce, Western Hemlock Spruce, California Hemlock Spruce, British Columbia Hemlock, Alaska Pine.

In General: Most abundant and of largest size on the coast slopes of Oregon and Washington.

Sometimes care is needed to distinguish this tree from Pacific Yew (*Taxus brevifolia*). Aids in this distinction are suggested by John A. Lee as follows:

"There is a plain distinction in the decidedly whitish appearance of the under side of the Western Hemlock foliage while the under side of the Yew needles is pale green. This pale green is much lighter than the green of their upper sides, but still evenly green and not whitish like the hemlock.

"Another distinction is that needles of the Yew take to a very sharp point while ends of the Hemlock needles are rather blunt."

HH154; Can48; P35; Sgt45; Su91

U. S. Forest Service Photo

J. S. Forest Service Photo

(*Tsuga Mertensiana*)

Usual Occurrence:
Geographical range—A to I inclusive
Elevation range   —5,000 to 7,000′ in Oregon (zones 2 and 3)
Foliage   —Needles, attached singly
Needles: ½ to ¾″ long, attached singly, but twig formation gives a tufted appearance. New needles are distinguished by their *whitish-gray color*, in contrast to the light green typical of young fir needles. This new needle color gives the tree a "spotty" appearance in summer. Foliage dark to pale blue-green. Needles blunt pointed, rounded, and plump looking. In this respect unlike Western Hemlock, but needles have the same small, distinct stems. (Star-like, in section, instead of being flat, like Lowland Hemlock.—JL)

Cones: Pendulous,* 1 to 3″ long, slender (¾″ diameter), purple before opening, much larger than Western Hemlock, tend to form in clusters. Usually so abundant★ as almost to cover the branchlets and to bend them down with their weight. Cones fall each winter. Some remain on the tree after maturity, open wide, while next crop is maturing. Bracts are one-fourth the length of the cone scales.

Bark: Dark, reddish brown, early broken and rough on young trees. On old trees, about 1 to 1½″ thick, deeply and narrowly furrowed with rough, hard ridges.

Tree: In maturity as much as 4 to 5′ × 70 to 100′ or more. Stunted form on bleak crests. ★Gracefully drooping, slender branches; crown extends to the ground; trunk rarely clear of branches for more than a few feet above the ground. Main branches are unique in having numerous, short, erect side branches. ("Drooping, frond-like lateral branches.")

Distribution: Southern Alaska to central California, eastward to Idaho and Montana. In Oregon at elevations 5,000 to 7,000′. ("Never below 3,000 to 4,000′ in Oregon."—JL) (At sea level in far north, at timberline in south—Su) Ascends to 10,000′ at southern limits.

Other Names: Black Hemlock, Sierra Hemlock, Patton Spruce, Williamson's Spruce, Hemlock Spruce, Alpine Spruce, Weeping Spruce, Alpine Hemlock.

In General: An alpine tree, has little resemblance to the better known Western Hemlock. On high, steep slopes, as a result of snow effect, the trunks are sometimes strongly bent down to their bases, in the form of a sled runner.

* An exception to the pendulous occurrence of cones is sometimes found in the exposed stunted trees, which have been known to have cones erect on the branchlets.

HH157; Can51; Ch85; P65; Sh17; Sgt46; Su95

(*Pseudotsuga*)

THE name "False Hemlock" (*Pseudotsuga*) indicates a relationship between this genus (of which two species are found in Pacific forests) and the true hemlocks. There is resemblance in the distinctly formed needle stems and in the habit and character of the cones. The resin vesicles of hemlock seeds, however, are absent in seeds of the False Hemlock. The latter have the resin pockets, or "blisters," in the bark of young trees, in this respect being similar to the firs. However, they are not firs and cannot be so classed.

The needles have traits that are also characteristic of several species of fir, *i.e.*, flat, blunt needles, attached singly and spirally on the branchlets. Because of a twist in their stems they often appear to grow mainly from two opposite sides and from the top of the branch. Needles of each year's growth remain on the tree usually 5 to 8 years.

The cones are pendulous, borne nearly or quite at the ends of twigs. The most distinctive characteristic of this species, however, is the form of the bracts.   *★No other cones of native conifers with persistent scales have protruding bracts of this shape.* (The larches have bracts of a different shape.)

Not only do bracts of the *Pseudotsuga* protrude conspicuously, but their tips have a strange triple point that is instantly recognized by one who has familiarized himself with this peculiarity. The cones mature in one season and soon afterward fall from the tree.

The two species of False Hemlock of which detailed descriptions follow are:

Douglas Fir...................................... Hf-1
   (*Pseudotsuga taxifolia*)
Bigcone Spruce................................... Hf-2
   (*Pseudotsuga macrocarpa*)

Asahel Curtis Photo

DOUGLAS FIR   Hf-1
(*Pseudotsuga taxifolia*)

Usual Occurrence:

Geographical range—A to L inclusive

Elevation range   —0 to 7,000′ or more (zones 1, 2, and 3)

Foliage   —Needles, attached singly

Needles: Usually ¾ to 1″ long, attached singly; straight, slightly grooved above; beneath, they have a white band on either side of a prominent midrib. Attached on all sides of twigs instead of in the form of flat sprays.   Occasionally persist longer than the 5- to 8-year average.   When pulled off they leave an oval scar on top of a small projection.

Cones: Reddish brown when mature, pendulous, 1½ to 4½″ long (commonly 2½ to 3″).   ★Three-pointed bracts protrude, often as much as ½″, beyond cone scales.   Cones grow nearly or quite at ends of twigs, ripen every year in August, soon open, shed their seeds, and a few weeks later drop from the tree.   Cones sometimes grow on trees only 12 years old.

Bark: Thick, soft in texture, easily cut with a knife.   On mature trees deeply furrowed.   Young trees have "balsam blisters" as do the firs.   "The heaviest bark of any tree in Canada, sometimes 10 to 12″ thick."—Can

Tree: In maturity 3½ to 6′ × 180 to 200′.   Peavey mentions (p. 25) a record-size tree 17 × 380′.   Long, clear, straight boles.   In open growths carries full crown with great, outstanding branches.   Foliage is a fresh green color; upper branches, uniformly spaced, point upward, especially on younger trees, giving the top of the crown a spire-like appearance.

Distribution: From central British Columbia to northern Mexico and from coast to continental divide.   Sea level to 7,000′ or more.   Often in pure, dense stands.   In the Sierra of California ranges up to 5,500′; in Colorado to 11,000′.

Other Names: Oregon Pine, Red Fir, Yellow Fir, Douglas-tree, Douglas Spruce, Red Pine, Puget Sound Pine, *Pseudotsuga Douglasii*, *Pseudotsuga mucronata*.

In General: This species has a close resemblance to the hemlocks, particularly in the needles and cones, but is distinct.   Douglas Fir and Bigcone Spruce are the only two native conifers with persistent cone scales that have protruding bracts of this shape.

The western rival of Longleaf Southern Pine.   Old growth gives fine-grained lumber of bright *yellow* hue.   Second growth timber (and heartwood of old growth) is of different character, giving a coarse-grained wood, hard and tough, of *reddish* color.   Hence the name "Red Fir."

The one-piece flagpole of the Oregon building at the Panama Pacific International Exposition in 1915 was Douglas Fir, 299′ 7″ in length.

HH145; Can60; Ch77; P23; Sh11; Sgt48; Su100

Hf-2

Paul Baumann Photos

(Pseudotsuga macrocarpa)

Usual Occurrence:
> Geographical range—K and L
> Elevation range   —1,500 to 6,000′ (zones 1 and 2)
> Foliage   —Needles, attached singly

Needles: Usually ¾ to 1¼″ long, attached singly, somewhat curved; grow on all sides of the branchlets, but by a strong twisting of their stems appear to come out mainly from two opposite sides of the twigs. They are more or less pointed, but not prickly.

Cones: Have protruding three-pointed bracts (like those of Douglas Fir) but have★ a size range of 3¾ to 6″ in length, averaging about twice as large as cones of the Douglas Fir. Not all the cones fall each year. Nuts, ½″ long, are dark chocolate-brown, shiny on the upper side which is in contrast to the dull under surface.

Bark: Blackish or dark red-brown; 2 to 5″ or more thick at base of trunk. Young trees have "balsam blisters" as do the firs.

Tree: Trunk tapers rapidly. Mature trees 1½ to 2′ × 30 to 60′ (sometimes 75′). General appearance of tree very *dissimilar* to Douglas Fir (Hf-1) on three counts:

1. Extremely irregular shape caused by great length of some branches while others are rather short, giving a ragged, scraggly appearance.

2. Grayish-green color, almost "dusty," in sharp contrast with fresh green of Douglas Fir.

3. Branches tend to droop.

Distribution: Southern and Lower California only, at elevations of 1,500 to 6,000′.

Other Names: Long considered a variety of Douglas Fir owing mainly to similar foliage and cones that are identical except for size. In reality it is a distinct species. The common name "Hemlock" is used by Sargent in listing this species.

In General: This tree and the Douglas Fir are the only native conifers with persistent cone scales that have protruding bracts of this shape.

HH150; Sgt49; Su104

(Juniperus)

F IVE species of juniper are native to the Pacific Coast.   Most of them are small or, at most, only medium-sized trees.   With one exception (the Dwarf Juniper, J-1) they have scale-like foliage much like that of the cypresses.   Unlike the cypresses, however, the junipers have cones that closely resemble berries and thus can be readily and positively distinguished from the cypresses.

Four of the five species are very similar in general appearance and require careful observation to make distinction between them.   The differences are brought out in the detailed descriptions of the several species that follow.

One of the junipers is of such special interest that the author invited a few comments on it from C. K. Bennett of San Francisco, who has observed and studied it for years throughout much of its range.   Mr. Bennett says of this remarkable species:

The Western Juniper (*Juniperus occidentalis*) grows to much larger sizes and attains greater age than one would conclude from reading what our tree authorities have published about it.   Despite the impression that this is a drawf tree, the writer knows of numerous specimens that range from 8 to 10′ in diameter and some are much larger.   One that he has visited several times (due west of the Sonora Pass, west side middle fork of Stanislaus River) and has measured carefully, is about 90′ high and has the following base dimensions:

MEASUREMENT LEVEL	DIAMETER	CIRCUMFERENCE (BARK MEASURE)
At ground level...............	21′ 6″*	57′ 6″
Breast high above ground......	14′ 2″	42′ 9″

* This is maximum; diameter is irregular.

The largest and oldest of these trees are found at elevations of 8,500 to 10,500′.   They prefer south or southwest exposures, are intolerant of being crowded and frequently the largest specimens grow out of rock in locations very much exposed to the elements.   The writer has a theory that they have lasted through the centuries in these isolated locations because there they have less exposure to forest fires.   At lower elevations some considerable stands of species show marked fire damage and are rarely of large size.   This suggests that a catastrophe agency accounts for their not attaining great age at the lower levels.

J

Geo. J. Young Photo

The rate of growth in the higher elevations is extremely slow.   The writer has cut limbs of 2 to 4″ diameter that show, on the windward side of the "streamlined" cross-section, as many as 400 annular rings per inch.   Altogether there are many indications of great age in these junipers at high elevation; the writer suspects that the one whose dimensions are given in the foregoing may be 4,000 to 5,000 years old.   If this is correct it may be one of these junipers and not a Big Tree that is "the oldest living thing."

The five species of junipers of which detailed descriptions follow are

Canadian Forest Service

DWARF JUNIPER   J-1

(Juniperus communis)

Usual Occurrence:

Geographical range—A to I inclusive

Elevation range   —8,300 to 9,800' in California (zone 3)

Foliage   —Scale-like

Needles:★ The chalky-white upper surfaces of these needles; their dark, lustrous green color; and keenly pointed, lance shape clearly distinguish this juniper from all other native species.   The needles are ⅓ to ½" long and spread widely (nearly at right angles) in groups of three from the triangular twigs.

Berries:★ About ¼" in diameter, mature at end of second summer (Sargent says third season), when they are a very dark blue—almost black— coated with whitish bloom.   The top of the berry is conspicuously marked by three blunt projections.   The soft flesh of the fruit is dry, resinous— aromatic—and contains from two to three hard, bony seeds.

Bark: About 1/16" thick, dark, reddish brown, separating irregularly into many loose, papery, persistent scales.

Tree: In Pacific forests barely more than a shrub, less than 5' high with numerous half-prostrate stems forming continuous tangled masses from 5 to 10 yd. across.   A very unsymmetrical trunk with conspicuous rounded ridges and grooves near the ground.   Only occasionally tree-like with a height of 10 to 20'.   Branchlets conspicuously three-angled.

Distribution: Alaska southward to central California and in the mountains of northern Arizona.   In Alaska at sea level; farther south usually well up toward timberline, particularly in California and Arizona.

Other Names: Ground Juniper, Scent Cedar, Scrub Juniper.

In General: Dwarf Juniper is more widely distributed than any other tree inhabiting the northern half of the globe.

HH219; Sgt80; Su176

U. S. Forest Service Photo

(*Juniperus scopulorum*)

Usual Occurrence:

Geographical range—B to G inclusive
Elevation range   —0 to 6,500′ (zones 1 and 2)
Foliage   —Scale-like

Leaves: The minute, scale-like leaves on the four-sided twigs and branch-lets are arranged★ in four rows of alternately opposite pairs. The back of each leaf or scale usually has a long indistinct pit. Note sharp points on scales of larger branchlets. Foliage is dark green, often paling to whitish.

Berries: About ¼ to ⅓″ in diameter. When mature, smooth, clear blue in color (from a whitish bloom which covers the thin blackish skin) and usually contain two seeds in a sweet, resinous pulp. Ripen at end of second season.

Bark: Stringy, has a seamy network pattern, broken on the surface into persistent shredded scales. Red-brown in color within and grayish outside.

Tree: In open situations 6 to 10″ × 15 to 20′ (sometimes 3 × 40′—Sgt). Bushy with a short trunk and long limbs which trend upward. Ends of branches and twigs are slender and drooping, giving a "weeping" effect. Often several main stems together.

Distribution: All along the coast in British Columbia, Washington, and Oregon. Found at elevations from a few hundred feet (Vancouver, B.C.) to 6,500′ (Steins Mountains, Oregon). Also along the eastern foothills of the Rockies in Alberta southward to western Texas.

Other Names: Rocky Mountain Red Cedar, Weeping Juniper, Red Cedar.

HH223; Sgt90; Su178

U. S. Forest Service Photos

WESTERN JUNIPER   J-3

(*Juniperus occidentalis*)

Usual Occurrence:

Geographical range—D to K inclusive

Elevation range   —2,500' up in California (zones 2 and 3)

Foliage   —Scale-like

Leaves: Scale-like, about ⅛" long, pale ashy-green; clasp the stiff twigs closely.   All leaves are prominently marked on the back by a glandular pit, whitish with resin.   "Groups of three leaves clasp the twigs successively, forming a rounded stem with six longitudinal rows of leaves."—Su.   Edges of leaves minutely notched.

Berries: About ¼ to ⅓" long, nearly globular, mature about Sept. 1 of second year, bluish black, covered with a whitish bloom.   Tough, thick skin, slightly marked at the tops by the tips of the female flower scales. Contain two or three bony, pitted, and grooved seeds.   Characteristics of berries distinguish this tree from the California Juniper, J-5.

Bark: Clear, light cinnamon-brown ½ to 1¼" thick.   Firm and stringy. Divided into flat ridges by wide furrows.

Tree: In maturity 1½* to 2½' × 15 to 30', rarely 60'.   A round-topped, open crown, extending to within a few feet of the ground.   Short, thick, conical trunk.   Rarely more than 4 to 8' of clear trunk.   Huge lower branches often rise from the base or trunk middle.   Tips of all branches turn upward, even in age.   Branches covered with thin, bright, red-brown bark, broken into loose, papery scales.   On dry rocky slopes and at northern limits of its range only a shrub.

Distribution: Southern California northward through Oregon and Washington.   Also found in Montana and Nevada.   In California elevation range is mostly above 6,000' although in vicinity of Mt. Shasta found as low as 2,500'.

Other Names: Sierra Juniper, Yellow Cedar, Western Cedar, Western Red Cedar.

In General: A high mountain tree.   Best means of distinguishing from the California Juniper is by comparison of berries.   However, the uniformly higher range of this tree makes unlikely confusion with California Juniper which ranges in a much lower zone.   An exceedingly long-lived tree; age range may be up to several thousand years.   "Attains its greatest trunk diameter on wind swept peaks of the California Sierra."—Sgt

* These diameters are greatly exceeded in certain favored locations at high elevations.   See comment by C. K. Bennett, p. 79.

Ch93; P37; Sgt85; Sh13; Su181

U. S. Forest Service Photo

(Juniperus utahensis)

Usual Occurrence:

 Geographical range—G to K inclusive
 Elevation range   —5,000 to 8,000' (zone 3)
 Foliage   —Scale-like

Leaves: Less than ⅛" long, sharp, scale-like, pale yellowish green.   Generally lacking the usual juniper pit or gland on the back.   Mostly in alternate, opposite pairs, closely overlapping each other in four rows. Sometimes in six rows, with three leaves at a joint.

Berries: Mature in fall of second year.   Covered with a whitish bloom over a smooth, red-brown, tough skin with a few projecting points.   Usually contain one seed (sometimes two) which is pointed at the top end and sharply angled.

Bark: About ¼" thick, ashy-gray or sometimes nearly white, cut into long, thin, persistent scales.

Tree: In maturity 4 to 8" × 6 to 12'.   A low, very short-trunked, bushy or many-stemmed tree.   Near the ground the trunk is divided by deep irregular fissures into broad, rounded ridges.   Broad, open head formed by many erect contorted branches.

Distribution: In California it is found along the Sierra from the southeastern part of the state to Lake Tahoe.   Thence its range extends northeast through Nevada to southwestern Idaho, also in Utah and Arizona.   Generally at elevations of 5,000 to 8,000'.

Other Names: Big-berry Juniper, Western Red Cedar, Desert Juniper.

In General: A tree of the high desert country.

HH222; Sgt82; Su186

Ntl. Park Service Photo

U. S. Forest Service Photo.

(Juniperus californica)

Usual Occurrence:

Geographical range—I to L inclusive

Elevation range   —400 to 4,000′ (zones 1 and 2)

Foliage   —Scale-like

Leaves: Scale-like, ⅛″ long, slightly keeled, conspicuously pitted with glands on the back, arranged three in a group on the stout twigs.   Leaves on young shoots longer (¼ to ½″) and keenly pointed.   Light yellow-green. Die and turn brown on the twig after 2 or 3 years.

Berries: About ¼ to ¾″ in length; light red-brown in color.   Markedly different from the bluish black, white-coated fruit of Western Juniper. Skin is loose, exceedingly thin and papery.   Seeds are one to two in number, more or less angular, grooved, and ridged.   Characteristics of the berries distinguish this tree from the Western Juniper, J-3.

Bark: Outwardly weathered to an ashy-gray color; red-brown beneath— a sharp contrast to the cinnamon-brown of Western Juniper.   Though scaly, the bark persists for many years.

Tree: In maturity 10 to 20″ × 20 to 25′.   The deeply infolded or fluted trunk★ is straight and less tapering than the fuller, more rounded, and only slightly grooved trunk of the Western Juniper.   Branches large and greatly distorted in old trees.

Distribution: Northern limit is in Lake County and Sierra foothills in Mariposa County, thence southward to northern Lower California. Generally at elevations between 2,000 and 4,000′.   (Sargent says 400 to 4,000′.)   Reaches its largest size on the Mojave desert.

Other Names: Desert White Cedar, White Cedar, Sweet-fruited Juniper, Sweet-berried Cedar.

In General: This species is found at a much lower elevation range than Western Juniper; the quickest means of distinguishing the two is by the fluted trunk of the California Juniper.

Sgt82; Su187

(*Larix*)

THE three species of larch native to Pacific Coast forests are trees of the north country.   All three extend their ranges north-ward into Canada, and one, together with the black and white spruces, grows in latitudes as far north as trees are found on this continent.

Generally speaking, larches are tall trees with straight, gradually tapering stems.   They can be readily distinguished from other cone-bearing trees by the fact that their foliage con-sists of needles attached in brush-like clusters of 12 to 40 at the ends of short, spur-like growths or knobs which stand out from the twigs.   The needles are attached without stalks.   All three species drop their needles each year and leave the tree bare dur-ing the winter.   Thus the larches are deciduous, in this respect unlike other native conifers which are all evergreens.

The following tabulation, which is a somewhat condensed form of data published by the Canadian Forest Service, lists traits of the three Pacific Coast species in a form convenient for comparison:

	Western Larch L-1 (*Larix occidentalis*)	Alpine Larch L-2 (*Larix Lyalli*)	Tamarack L-3 (*Larix laricina*)
Bark	Thicker than that of the other two larches	Thin, rarely over 1″ even on old trees	Thin
Twigs	Crown composed of a very few hori-zontal branches	Branches hang down conspicuously and turn up at ends	
	Twigs brittle	Twigs very tough	Twigs slender and pliable
Needles	Triangular cross-section, 1 to 2″ long	Four-sided cross-section, 1 to 1½″ long	Triangular cross-section, ¾ to 1¼″ long
	Cross-section shows no resin ducts	Cross-section shows two resin ducts, one in each of two corners	Cross-section shows two resin ducts near outside edge
Cones	From 1 to 1½″ long. Pointed bracts project beyond the scales but as a rule not bent so much as those of the Alpine Larch	From 1½ to 2″ long. Pointed bracts project beyond the scale and bend back	Spherical, rarely more than ½″ long. No bracts visible

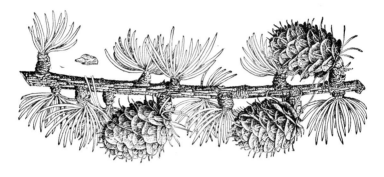

U. S. Forest Service Photos

(Larix occidentalis)

Usual Occurrence:
  Geographical range—B to F inclusive
  Elevation range   —2,000 to 7,000′ (zones 2 and 3)
  Foliage   —Needles, in clusters of 14 to 30
            on spur branchlets

Needles: Pale yellow-green. In clusters of 14 to 30, 1 to $1\frac{1}{4}''$ long. Turn bright lemon-yellow, and all fall off each winter. Needles are sharp pointed, flatly triangular, and distinctly ridged or keeled on their inner surface.

Cones: 1 to $1\frac{1}{2}''$ long. Soft, woolly, whitish hairs coat the outside of the cone scales below the centers. Pointed bracts protrude. Cone scales broader than they are long.

Bark: Middle-aged and old trunks have reddish-brown bark 3 to 6″ thick which is furrowed deeply near the base where ridges are strikingly massive. Often has oblong plates as much as 2′ long; is highly resistant to fire. Young trees have thin, scaly bark of grayish brown.

Tree: In maturity 3 to 5′ × 200′. Sometimes attain diameters of 8′. Trunk straight, tapering, often clear for 50 to 100′. Crown short, narrow, and open, running to a point.

Distribution: British Columbia south to northern Oregon, east as far as Montana. Usually at elevations between 2,000 and 7,000′.

Other Names: Tamarack, Western Tamarack, Hackmatack, Oregon Larch, Red American Larch, Montana Larch.

HH123; P56; Sgt32; Su68

U. S. Forest Service Photos

Usual Occurrence:

Geographical range—B, C, D, E

Elevation range   —6,000 to 7,000' (zone 3)

Foliage   —Needles, in clusters of 30 to 40 or more
on spur branchlets

Needles: 30 or 40 or more in a cluster, more or less four-angled and about 1 to $\frac{5}{8}''$ long.   Foliage distinctly light bluish green, turning bright lemon-yellow and falling off late in autumn.   Its color distinguishes it even on distant, high, and inaccessible peaks and crests.   "A cross-section of a leaf shows two resin ducts, one in each of the two angles; that of the Western Larch shows only one duct."—Can

Cones:★ About $1\frac{1}{2}$ to 2" long.   Bristly bracts of a deep purple project from among the cone scales.   Margins and outer surfaces of cone scales have a fringe of tangled, fine white wool.   Conspicuous, long-tipped bracts.

Bark: Ranges up to $\frac{7}{8}''$ thick.   Indistinctly furrowed, has irregular ridges of loose, flat scales which are deep purplish or reddish brown.

Tree: Stunted in appearance, often crooked and bent.   In maturity 10 to 24" × 30 to 40'.   Some of the branches are large and long, giving unsymmetrical appearance.   In contrast with the brittle branches of the Western Larch these branches are tough and limber.   New branch shoots have a coating of fine white wool.

Distribution: At timberline along continental divide, Alberta, eastern British Columbia, northern Montana, and even occasionally in Washington and Oregon as far south as Mt. Hood.   Elevation range:

British Columbia........................ 6,500 to 7,000'

Washington............................ 5,000 to 7,400'

Other Names: Tamarack, Mountain Larch, Lyall's Larch, Woolly Larch (from coating on new shoots).

In General: Strictly an alpine tree—an aid in distinguishing it from Western Larch.

HH125; Sgt33; Su71

U. S. Forest Service Photos

(Larix laricina)
including var. *L. alaskensis*

Usual Occurrence:

      Geographical range—A

      Elevation range   —(zone 1)

      Foliage   —Needles, in clusters of 12 to 20

                      on spur branchlets

Needles: Scattered singly on vigorous leading shoots, but elsewhere in clusters of 12 to 20. Indistinctly triangular in cross-section, convex on the upper side with a ridge beneath. Needles deciduous annually; turn yellow and fall in September or October, $\frac{3}{4}$ to $1\frac{1}{4}''$ long.

Cones:★ Usually $\frac{1}{2}$ to $\frac{3}{4}''$ long, have thin papery scales (about 20), scales twice as long as the bracts, mature in early autumn of first year. Usually fall in second year.

Bark: About $\frac{1}{2}$ to $\frac{3}{4}''$ thick, with rather bright, reddish-brown scales which flake off abundantly.

Tree: In the far Northwest this is a small tree, in maturity often only 1 to $3'' \times 6$ to $10'$. East of the Rockies and in the Great Lakes country it becomes 20 to $24'' \times 60$ to $80'$. Trees 10 to $12''$ in diameter are found to have an age of 60 to 75 years.

Distribution: Pacific slope of Rocky Mountains in Alaska, extending northward nearly to Bering Sea. A tree preferring low elevations.

Other Names: Larch, (*Larix americana*) Hackmatack.

Alaska Larch (*Larix alaskensis*) not considered distinct from Tamarack by many authorities, has somewhat shorter needles, and the cones have wider, shield-shaped bracts. The range of this variety is restricted to coastal Alaska from Cook Inlet north to the Yukon.

HH120 & 126; Sgt31; Su73

(Pinus)

T HERE are some 70 species of pines known throughout the world. Of this number 34 are found in the United States, and 17 of these, which occur in forests of the Pacific slope, are treated in this manual.

The needles of pines grow in bundles of two, three, four, or five, excepting one species which has needles attached separately. Needles produced in one season remain on the pines from 2 to 6 or 8 years.   Hence the older the tree, the fewer the needles near the trunk.   Needle bundles of all 17 pines are circular in section.

Cones mature in from 2 to 3 years.   Some remain on the trees only a few weeks after ripening; others persist for many years. In some species the cones are attached so firmly that many do not fall after maturity but remain in place and eventually are partly or even entirely enveloped by the annual diameter increase of the branches on which they grew.

At maturity most cones open under heat of the sun's rays. Some rarely open their cones except under the heat of a forest fire. This latter quality makes for reseeding after destruction of a forest by fire.

The seventeen species of pine of which detailed descriptions follow are:

P-1

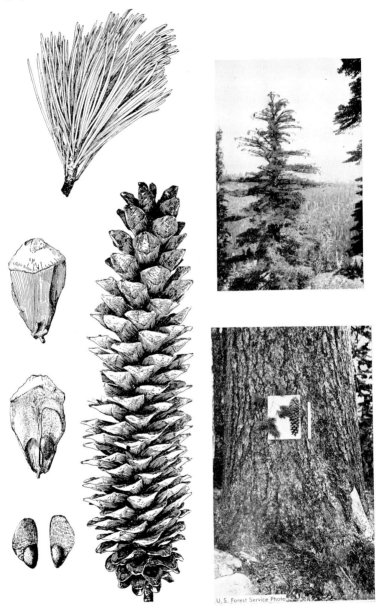

U. S. Forest Service Photo

Usual Occurrence:

Geographical range—F to L inclusive

Elevation range   —3,000 to 6,000' (zones 2 and 3)

Foliage   —Needles, in bundles of 5

Needles: 5 in a bundle, 2 to 4″ long, attached to all sides of twigs. Needles thicker and more rigid than in Western White Pine; remain on twig through third year.

Cones:★ Few, pendulous, on tips of branches, 8 to 12″ long (rarely 24″), 4 to 6″ thick when well opened. Commonly attached near summit of tree. Seeds thin-shelled, about ⅓″ long, winged, edible. Sometimes cone scale tips are pointed, more often have scar-like umbo. Before maturing, cones are purple-brown and stand erect. By August of second year they become pendulous. In October scales expand and release winged seeds. Cones remain on tree 2 to 3 years.

Bark: On mature trees deeply furrowed and broken into characteristic "turtle-back" plates, 2 to 4″ thick, reddish brown in color. On young trees and near tops of old trees bark is silver-grey, much like that on young firs.

Tree: Trunks of mature trees almost cylindrical—straight and clear, often for 100' or more. Mature trees 4 to 7′ × 160 to 180′ (max. 12 × 200 or 220′—Sgt). A characteristic trait which distinguishes this tree from all associated species is the irregular crown★ consisting of horizontal arms of unequal length; frequently the crown is flat-topped. Limbs are rather uniformly clothed with needles, giving a dense, furry appearance to the foliage. This is in striking contrast to the "tufty" appearance of the Western Yellow Pine.

Distribution: Oregon to Lower California. Elevation range, 2,000 to 11,000' (Oregon). Ordinarily 3,000 to 9,000'; best development at 3,500 to 6,000' in the North, 5,500 to 8,000' in the South. Sometimes as low as 2,500' in California. Never occurs in pure stands.

Other Names: Big Pine, Shade Pine, Great Sugar Pine.

In General: The largest of the pines. Some resemblance to Western White Pine; distinguish by comparing cones and needles.

Ch13; HH57; J56; P43; Sgt5; Su23

Photo by Shoeb

W. L. Huber Photo

U. S. Forest Service Photo

U. S. Forest Service Photo

WESTERN YELLOW PINE   P-2
(*Pinus ponderosa*)

Usual Occurrence:
Geographical range—C to L inclusive
Elevation range   —0 to 7,000′ in Oregon (zones 1, 2, and 3)
Foliage   —Needles, in bundles of 3

Needles: 3 in a bundle (occasionally 2, rarely 4 and 5), 4 to 11″ long. Have a tendency to group themselves in tufts at the ends of naked branches. This "tufty" appearance of foliage is a characteristic trait of mature Yellow Pines. Mostly deciduous in third season.

Cones: From 2¾ to 5¾″ long and 1½ to 2″ thick. Cone scales have thick tips with umbo in form of short curved thorn on under side of tip; this thorn turns outward, making cones prickly to the touch, in contrast with cones of Jeffrey Pine. Usually set in a mass of needles at the ends of the branches. Cones all fall off before early winter. When open, break through near the base and fall, leaving basal scales on the limb. (Sargent says cones are often clustered.)

Bark: 2 to 4″ thick, on mature trees, divided by fissures into broad plates of bright, cinnamon-red which may be 1 to 4′ long × ½ to 1½′ wide. Until trees are 80 to 100 years old, the bark is less broken and dark brown to nearly black.

Tree: In maturity 3 to 4′ × 125 to 140′ (max. 8 × 230′). Bole is cylindrical, long and clear, in dense stands. Crown on upper one-third only. Crowns of young trees conical; mature trees usually have flat tops. Branches horizontal or turned upward at the ends. Isolated trees have very long branches, sometimes nearly to the ground.

Distribution: Southern British Columbia to northern Mexico, east to Black Hills of South Dakota. Either in wet or dry climates. More widely distributed than any other North American conifer. Altitude ranges:

British Columbia and Washington....... Sea level to 6,200′
Oregon............................... Sea level to 7,000′
North Idaho.......................... 2,000 to 7,000′
Northern California.................. 300 to 7,000′
Southern California.................. 4,000 to 9,000′
Arizona.............................. 5,000 to 8,000′

Other Names: Pondosa Pine, Ponderosa Pine, California White Pine, Western Soft Pine, Black Jack, Black Pine, Jack Pine, Bull Pine, Yellow Pine, British Columbia Soft Pine, Longleaved Pine, Red Pine, Pitch Pine, Western Pitch Pine, Heavy Pine.

In General: Young shoots have a strong odor when bruised. The Forest Service says that this tree provides 50 per cent of average annual lumber cut in California and forms about 25 per cent of the timber stand in that state. See P-3 for distinctions between P-2 and P-3.

Ch17; HH96; J62; P30; Sgt12; Su42

P-3

W. L. Huber Photo

U. S. Forest Service Photo

· 106 ·

(*Pinus Jeffreyi*)

Usual Occurrence:

        Geographical range—G to L inclusive

        Elevation range   —3,000 to 8,000' (zones 2 and 3)

        Foliage   —Needles, in bundles of 3

Needles: 3 in a bundle, 4 to 9″ long, stiffer and more elastic than Yellow Pine, persist 6 to 9 years.

Cones:★ 5 to 8″ long (5 to 15″—HH) which is much larger than those of the Yellow Pine. As compared with the Yellow Pine, the Jeffrey cones are much denser; ★they are shaped like the old-fashioned beehive. Prickle of the umbo often more slender than on Yellow Pine but turns inward, and hence cones can be handled without the prickly feel typical of Yellow Pine cones.

Bark: In mature trees reddish to almost black, broken into narrow plates; in young trees, white.

Tree: Somewhat smaller than the Yellow Pine; ordinarily 60 to 120' and sometimes 170' high. Has trunk diameter relatively greater, with respect to height, than the Yellow Pine.

Distribution: Through the mountains of southern Oregon and southward to Lower California. Although the elevation range is 3,000 to 8,000', the best commercial growth is between 5,000 and 6,500'.

Other Names: *Pinus ponderosa* var. *Jeffreyi*, Bull Pine, Black Pine, Pinos, Truckee Pine, Sapwood Pine.

In General: Harlow and Harrar say: "Trained observers rarely experience any difficulty in distinguishing between Jeffrey and Ponderosa Pines in the field. For convenience the principal features of these two pines are repeated in the following table:"

	Jeffrey Pine	Ponderosa Pine
Needles	Blue-green (glaucous in one variety), occasionally twisted, persistent 6 to 9 years	Yellow-green to gray-green, persistent about 3 years
Buds	Nonresinous	Profusely dotted with resin droplets
Young stems	With a purplish hue	Brownish green
Inner bark	Grayish to brownish tan	Light yellow to golden-yellow
Odor of crushed stems	Violet-like or pineapple-like	Turpentine-like
Cones	5 to 15″ long, scales armed with long prickles	3 to 6″ long, scales armed with short prickles

Ch21; HH101; J65; Sgt13; Sh1; Su47

P-4

U. S. Forest Service Photo

(Pinus contorta)

Usual Occurrence:
Geographical range—A to L inclusive
Elevation range   —Sea level to high elevations (zones 1, 2, and 3)
Foliage   —Needles, in bundles of 2

Needles: 2 in a bundle, 1 to 3″ long; densely clothe the branchlets. Foliage of coast (or beach) variety is dark yellow-green. Foliage of mountain form distinctively a bright yellow-green. Persistent sheath at base of each bundle.

Cones: 1 to 2″ long, numerous. Thorny umbo, hooked on scales at base of cone. This tree produces cones at the remarkably early age of 7 to 10 years. Cones of mountain form fall freely, sometimes carpeting the ground under the tree; in the beach form (and var. *Bolanderi*) they persist, sometimes remaining attached to the branch unopened for 15 to 20 years or more.

Bark: Bark of beach and mountain forms differ: in the beach form it is ¾ to 1″ thick, deeply furrowed and transversely fissured, reddish brown to black, only superficially scaly. The mountain form has bark only ¼″ thick, often a light brown to orange color and scaly to the point of being scabby, even near the top and on young trees.

Tree: Beach form often is diminutive, scrubby, and distorted. The mountain form of mature tree is 12 to 18″ × 90′ (max. 6 × 150′). Inland form has tall slender bole, rounded crown. Much-forked branches often extend nearly to base of stem.

Distribution: From Alaska to northern part of Lower California. Eastward to the Dakotas. Sea level to 11,000′ (in southern territory). Most often on the edges of mountain meadows. Occurs in pure stands of dense forests, also mixes with other trees. "Attains greatest size and development in southern Sierra Nevada at elevations between 8,000 and 9,500′."—Sgt

Other Names: Beach form: Beach Pine, Sand Pine, Scrub Pine, Tamarack Pine, Knotty Pine, Henderson's Pine. (In the area of the Mendocino coastal plain known as the "White Plains," the Beach Pine is replaced by a dwarf variety, generally less than 5′ tall, known as *Pinus contorta* var. *Bolanderi* or Bolander's Pine.)

Mountain form: *Pinus contorta* var. *Murrayana* or var. *Latifolia*, *Pinus Murrayana*, Tamarack, Spruce Pine, Murray Pine.

In General: Beach and mountain forms of *Pinus contorta* are not really separable; Sudworth says that those who attempt it "would have taken the broader view had they been able to study the trees as they grow in all their retreats." All differences "are not too great to be consistently merged in one polymorphous species."

Ch37; HH105; Sgt23; Sh7; Su49; P45

U. S. Forest Service Photo

WESTERN WHITE PINE   P-5

(*Pinus monticola*)

Usual Occurrence:

    Geographical range—B to K inclusive

    Elevation range   —Sea level to 10,000′ (zones 1, 2, and 3)

    Foliage   —Needles, in bundles of 5

Needles: 5 in a bundle, rarely 4. 1 to 4″ long, pointed, very slender. Shorter than those of Sugar Pine. Sheathed at base by thinnish, narrow, deciduous scales, some of which are shorter than those of the Sugar Pine.

Cones: 6 to 8 and rarely 10″ long ("up to 18″ "—Can). In clusters of one to seven, borne near the ends of high branches, pendulous, on long stalks. ★Very slender when closed and usually curved toward the tip. Scales thin, smooth, widening from the base to the rounded apex. A terminal, scar-like umbo. Cones similar to but smaller than Sugar Pine cones. Two seeds, about ⅓″ long, under each cone scale. Seed wings are sharper pointed than those of the Sugar Pine.

Bark: On mature trees broken into small square blocks; ¾ to 1¼″ thick. Color varies from cinnamon in open stands to grayish purple in dense forests. Divided into small, nearly square plates by deep longitudinal and cross fissures—covered with small scales.

Tree: In maturity 2 to 3′ × 100′ or more (4 to 8′ × 150′—Sgt). Tall, slender bole peculiarly short branched; narrow, symmetrical crown with slender branches, horizontal or somewhat drooping. Very top may have a cluster of ascending or semi-upright cone-bearing branches. Usually one or several stout branches extend horizontally 10 to 15′ beyond other branches. This peculiarity is visible as far as the tree can be seen.

Distribution: Nowhere abundant except in small patches. This tree is primarily a mountain type, but in the Puget Sound basin and the Olympic Peninsula it occurs frequently at sea level. Elevation range is as follows:

British Columbia, Washington, and Oregon, west of the Cascades	Sea level to 3,000′
East of the Cascades and in Idaho and Montana	2,000 to 7,000′
California	5,000 to 10,000′

Other Names: Silver Pine, White Pine, Idaho White Pine, Mountain White Pine, Mountain Pine, Little Sugar Pine, Soft Pine, Fingercone Pine, Mountain Weymouth Pine.

In General: A tree in many of its characteristics similar to Sugar Pine. Age ranges from 200 to 500 years. "Snow falls throughout its range." Very young twigs and shoots are covered with a fine reddish down which helps to distinguish this tree from similar species.

Ch41; HH54; J56; Sgt4; Sh7; Su20; P47

(Pinus attenuata)

Usual Occurrence:

Geographical range—G to L inclusive
Elevation range   —1,500 to 4,000' (zone 1)
Foliage   —Needles, in bundles of 3

Needles: 3 in a bundle, 3 to 7″ long (mainly 3½ to 5″). Slender, rigid, light green.

Cones: 3 to 6″ long, slender; scales moderately thickened at tip except on outside at base where they are raised into conspicuous rounded or pointed knobs. Cones adhere to the branches indefinitely, seldom opening until the tree is killed. ★"Clusters of them, rigidly attached and bent down, encircle the main stems of even small trees (5 to 8' high) and are the most striking characteristics of this pine." Umbos small and slender; prickles usually deciduous.

Bark: Thin (¼ to ½″ thick), dull brown, shallowly ridged and furrowed, mainly near the ground. The ridges have large loose scales.

Tree: In maturity 6 to 12″ × 15 to 30'. Exceptional trees, 20″ × 80'. The slender branches curve outward and upward. Old trees often have the trunk forked near its middle. Branches of young trees are attached to the trunk in regular whorls.

Distribution: Southwestern Oregon to southern California. Elevation range, 1,500 to 4,000' on rocky slopes and ridges in the most hopelessly inhospitable and desolate mountain regions.

Other Names: Scrub Pine (*Pinus tuberculata*).

In General: Valued chiefly as a ground cover following forest fires because cones usually do not open until the death of the tree. Many trees show that they have retained their cones for nearly 50 years.

Ch33; HH112; J77; P66; Sgt19; Sh7; Su62

Usual Occurrence:

 Geographical range—H, I, J, K

 Elevation range —1,000 to 4,000′ (zone 1)

 Foliage   —Needles, in bundles of 3

Needles: In bundles of 3. 7 to 13½″ long, drooping. Gray-green in color and sparse. ★"You can fairly see through a Digger Pine." Needles fall usually in third and fourth years.

Cones: 6 to 10″ long, 5 to 7″ thick, on stalks about 2″ long. Mature in second season, but remain on tree 1 to 7 years after releasing the seeds, which are very hard shelled and about ¾″ long. Some cone scale tips develop into triangular hooks. When cones fall, a few scales from base usually remain on the stalk. Cones frequently have pitch on scale tips.

Bark: Mature trees have bark 1½ to 2″ thick: dull gray-brown, scaly, deeply ridged, fissures slightly tinged with red.

Tree: 1 to 4′ × 40 to 50′, sometimes 90′. Trunk usually branches, 5 to 15′ from the ground, into a cluster of secondary stems which form a broom-like top. One rarely sees a tree in which trunk axis bears only lateral branches through the crown.

Distribution: *Spec.* In the dry, hot foothills of central California. Usual elevation range 500 to 4,000′. Always in scattered growths. Ranges south to the Tehachapi and north to Sacramento River canyon.

Other Names: Sabin's Pine, Bull Pine, Squaw Pine, Nut Pine, Gray Pine, Grayleaf Pine, Blue Pine.

In General: The gray, thin foliaged crown of one or two long upright forks, with big, dark cones that can be seen half a mile away, distinguish it at long distances from associated trees. When planted for ornament in rich, cultivated soil, the foliage becomes much stouter and thicker, giving the tree an entirely different aspect from one grown in its dry native habitat; the cones of such cultivated trees are usually smaller. It is named after the Digger Indians of California who used the seed for food.

Ch29; HH110; J68; Sgt20; Sh3; Su54

P-8

MONTEREY PINE   P-8

(*Pinus radiata*)

Usual Occurrence:

Geographical range—J

Elevation range   —A few hundred feet above sea level (zone 1)

Foliage   —Needles, in bundles of 3

Needles: Bundles of 3 and 2, from 3 to 6″ long.   Make a rich, dark green foliage.   Deciduous in third season.

Several hundred foliage samples of this species, examined by the author, had many of the needles attached in bundles of 2; in some samples the 2-needle bundles constituted 75 per cent of the total.   Needle grouping is not a stable and dependable trait in this tree.

Cones: 3 to 7″ long.   Frequently curved.   Scales on outer side near base conspicuously developed or swollen at tip with pyramidal tubercle armed with prickle which usually weathers off.   Closed★ cones persist for many years on the tree.   Scales of reflexed cones have flat smooth edges.

Bark: Roughly fissured, 1½ to 2″ thick, hard, and more nearly black than that of any other California pine.

Tree: In maturity 1 to 4′ × 90 to 100′ in sheltered locations.   (60 to 80′ high on coast, where it is distorted and flat topped.)

Distribution: Not found more than a few hundred feet above sea level, then only in a few limited areas of central California, particularly near Monterey and San Simeon.   A closely allied form (var. *binnata*) occurs on Guadalupe Island, Lower California.   This variety has most of its leaves in bundles of two.

Other Names: *Pinus insignis.*

In General: Much used for windbreak and cover in San Francisco Bay region.   Wider horticultural distribution than any other California conifer. A short-lived tree.   Maturity usually 80 to 100 years and rarely passing the age of 150 years.

HH114; J76; Sgt19; Sh4; Su58

Usual Occurrence:

    Geographical range—I to L inclusive

    Elevation range   —0 to 1,000′ (zone 1)

    Foliage   —Needles, in bundles of 2

Needles: 2 in a bundle, $3\frac{1}{2}$ to $5\frac{1}{2}''$ long, stiff, deep yellow-green. Begin to fall in second year. Foliage is conspicuously dense on the extremities of the numerous branches.

Cones: 2 to $3\frac{1}{2}''$ long, attached at a sharp angle, thus making lack of symmetry a characteristic trait; usually in clusters. Scales much thickened on outside of cone and at base often armed with spur-like spines. The cones are characterized by their indefinite persistence. A singular fact is that they rarely or never are imbedded in the stems of the trees, as is the case of other pines with persistent cones. The stems of the cones are soon broken by the growing branch, and thereafter the cone is held lightly by the living bark. Seeds, nearly triangular, have a roughish surface.

Bark: 4 to 6″ thick, deeply furrowed and rough, with purple-brown scales.

Tree: In maturity 1 to 2′ × 30 to 60′ (max. 3 × 80′). A dense crown, rounded at the top, with stout branches extending to the ground.

Distribution: California coast region from Mendocino County to San Luis Obispo County, also Lower California coast and Cedros Island. From near sea level to elevation of 1,000′ and extending about 1 mile inland.

Other Names: Bishop's Pine, Swamp Pine, Dwarf Marine Pine, Obispo Pine, Bull Pine, Scrub Pine.

In General: On Santa Cruz Island (30 miles offshore at Santa Barbara) two pines are found. One is the typical Pricklecone Pine with unsymmetrical cones whose scale tips are thickened. The other, a closely related species, differs in having *symmetrical* cones with all the cone scales *flat*. This latter pine has been named *Pinus remorata*.

HH115; Sgt28; Sh7; Su65

(Pinus aristata)

Usual Occurrence:

Geographical range—I, J, K

Elevation range   —7,000 to 11,000' (zone 3)

Foliage   —Needles, in bundles of 5

Needles: Usually 5 to a bundle, $1\frac{1}{4}$ to $1\frac{1}{2}''$ long, attached in clusters. Deep green foliage, densely clustered at ends of twigs in long, compact, brush-like tufts.

Cones: Usually $2\frac{1}{2}$ to $3\frac{1}{2}''$ long. Scales tipped with long, sharp, thin★ prickles. Hang pendant on very tips of branchlets. Open and scatter seeds about Oct. 1.

Bark: Thin on young trees. On old trees $\frac{1}{2}$ to $\frac{3}{4}''$ thick, dull reddish brown, shallowly furrowed; the main flat ridges irregularly connected by narrower slanting divisions. Surface covered with small scales.

Tree: In maturity 12 to $18'' \times 15$ to 30'. An irregular bushy tree with a short, thick trunk. Short, stout branches in regular whorls while young.

Distribution: Found mainly at high elevations (7,000 to 11,000'). Colorado, southern Utah, southern Nevada, and southeastern California and on San Francisco peaks in northern Arizona. In California reported locations are Panamint Mountains (7,800 to 10,800'), White and Inyo Mountains, high Sierra east of Yosemite.

Other Names: Foxtail Pine, Hickory Pine.

In General: An alpine species; only a straggler in Pacific forests.

Ch57: HH71: Sgt8: Sh5: Su37

Geo. D. Whittle Photo.

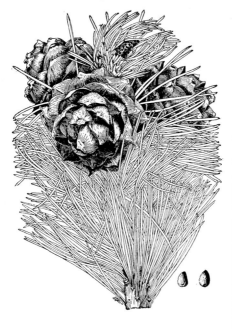

U. S. Forest Service Photo

White-bark Pine   P-11
(*Pinus albicaulis*)

Usual Occurrence:
    Geographical range—C to K inclusive
    Elevation range   —5,000 to 12,000′ (zone 3)
    Foliage   —Needles, in bundles of 5

Needles: In bundles of 5, from 1 to 2½″ long, stout, rigid, slightly incurving, dark green, persisting 5 to 8 years but clothing only the tips of the slowly growing branchlets.

Cones: Deep purple when growing on the tree, brown when dry, very thick scales. 1 to 3″ long and nearly as thick (ovoid or subglobose, short, acute umbo). Needles and cones cluster at ends of branches. Cones remain closed and retain the seeds for several years.

Bark: Thin and silvery, rarely more than ½″ thick. (Young tree bark is pinkish.—GY) Some old trees in exposed locations have light reddish bark. At the base narrow cracks break the bark into whitish scales.

Tree: Dwarfed into shapeless shrubs at highest elevations but in more sheltered spots have been found 2′ in diameter and 50′ high (2 to 4′ × 60′ as a maximum.—Sgt). Dwarf trees often have two or three main stems from the base and often crowns on the ground like low, flat tables over which one may walk readily.

Distribution: High Sierra passes, usually at or near timberline. 5,000 to 11,000′ in northern ranges and 9,500 to 12,000′ in the south. Not below elevation 7,500′ on Rubicon Peak near Lake Tahoe, California. Southwest limit about Mt. Whitney. North into British Columbia and east into Montana.

Other Names: Dwarf Pine, White-stemmed Pine, Scrub Pine.

In General: Catkins bright pink. Reproduction is always poor; growth is very slow; maturity is reached in about 250 years, but trees live to much greater age.

Ch53; HH63; J58; Sgt6; Sh7; Su30

Geo. D. Whittle Photo

U. S. Forest Service Photo

(Pinus Torreyana)

Usual Occurrence:

    Geographical range—L

    Elevation range   —0 to 100' (zone 1)

    Foliage   —Needles, in bundles of 5

Needles: In bundles of 5, from 8 to 12″ long, thick, stiff, and strong; have sharp points. Stand out from all sides of branches, giving boughs a stiff, coarse appearance. Because needles do not persist long, the foliage tends to cluster around bough tips thus giving a tufted appearance to branch ends. The young needles have a remarkably long sheath at their base (1¼″ or more), light brown in color. When needles are old, the sheath turns darker (almost black) and has a tendency to be torn and ragged at its outer end.

Cones: 4 to 6″ long, subglobose, on long stalks. Russet or chocolate-brown, strongly attached; scales at apex thickened into heavy pyramids, armed with small spines. Mostly deciduous in fourth year. Seeds ¾ to 1″ long, edible raw or roasted.

Bark: About 1″ thick, roughly and deeply broken into ridges with wide, flat, pale reddish-brown scales.

Tree: Bent by sea winds. In maturity a crooked tree of irregular shape, 8 to 14″ × 20 to 35'. Sheltered spots sometimes produce a tree 50 to 60' high.

Distribution: *Spec.* Found near the sea only in San Diego County and Santa Rosa Island. (Sea level to about 100'.)

Other Names: Soledad Pine, Del Mar Pine, Lone Pine.

In General: The rarest of California pines. ★Its only known occurrence on the mainland is in San Diego County near the mouth of the Soledad River, now protected in an extensive municipal park.

HH113; J70; Sgt30; Sh7; Su41

U. S. Forest Service Photo

Usual Occurrence:

        Geographical range—I to L inclusive

        Elevation range   —2,500 to 6,000' (zones 1 and 2)

        Foliage   —Needles, in bundles of 3

Needles: 3 in a bundle, from $6\frac{1}{2}$ to 12″ long (average 9″), stiffer and heavier than those of Western Yellow Pine, as are also the branches and twigs. Needles fall in third or fourth seasons.

Cones:★ 9 to 14″ long, very thick and heavy; scales terminating in a broad, incurved, hooked claw $\frac{1}{2}$ to $1\frac{1}{2}$″ long, especially at base of cone. The heaviest cones of any American pine; sometimes weigh 4 to 5 lb., green. When falling, cones break through near the base, leaving basal scales on the limb, as do cones of the Yellow Pine.

Bark: Usually $1\frac{1}{2}$ to 2″ thick, very dark or blackish brown, roughly broken to form irregular network of longitudinal fissures.

Tree: In maturity $1\frac{1}{2}$ to $2\frac{1}{2}'$ × 40 to 60'. Usually large, long lower branches bend down, often to the ground and have an upward curve at their ends. Immense bunches of erect, stiff needles form the ends of the branches.

Distribution: Common in the coast ranges of southern and Lower California, 2,500 to 6,000'. A few trees on the north side of Mt. Diablo (east of San Francisco) mark its northern limit. Most abundant on San Jacinto and San Bernardino ranges at elevations of about 5,000'.

Other Names: Coulter Pine, Pitch Pine, Nut Pine.

In General: Although it has a general resemblance to young Yellow Pine, this tree is easily distinguished by its heavier masses of foliage, stout twigs, and great cones which are "horribly armed" with talon-like appendages on the scale tips.

Ch25; HH109; J67; Sgt21; Sh2: Su57

P-14

U.S. Forest Service Photos

(Pinus flexilis)

Usual Occurrence:

Geographical range—B to L inclusive

Elevation range   —7,000' up (zone 3)

Foliage   —Needles, in bundles of 5

Needles: In bundles of 5, growing in close masses, often curving, 1½ to 3″ long, on flexible trailing branches. Needles densely clothe ends of the branchlets, forming a sort of brush. Needles are stout, rigid, dark green, deciduous in fifth and sixth years.

Cones: Buff to olive-buff, globose to long ovate. 4 to 10″ long (2 to 5″—J). Require 2 years to mature. By early winter of second year have fallen from the tree. Scar-like umbo. The much-thickened tips of the cone scales are a trait that helps to distinguish this tree from similar species.

Bark: Color of bark on young branches is very light; that on the main stem is 1 to 2″ thick, dark brown, deeply furrowed, and broken crosswise into nearly square plates, covered by small scales.

Tree: Ordinarily 1 to 3′ × 25 to 30′ (2 to 5′ × 40 to 50′—Sgt). Green twigs are so limber★ that they can almost be tied in knots without breaking. Stout, persistent branches ultimately form a wide, round-topped head.

Distribution: Distinctively a tree of the desert ranges, found only at high elevations, usually above 7,000'; in California prefers deserts of high elevation or mountains bordering the desert. Extends east to the Rocky Mountains and ranges from Alberta to New Mexico. Reaches largest size in Arizona and New Mexico.

Other Names: White Pine, Rocky Mountain Pine, Rocky Mountain White Pine (*Pinus strobiformis*), Bull Pine, Arizona Flexilis Pine.

Ch49; HH61; J59; Sgt6; Sh5; Su27

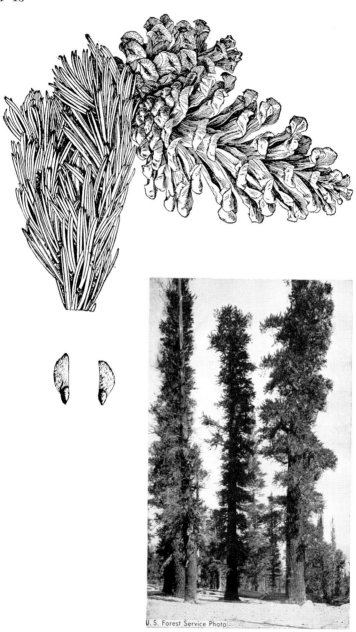

U. S. Forest Service Photo

(*Pinus Balfouriana*)

Usual Occurrence:
  Geographical range—H to K inclusive
  Elevation range   —5,000 to 11,500′ (zone 3)
  Foliage   —Needles, in bundles of 5
Needles: In bundles of 5, from ¾ to 1½″ long, curved and crowded closely to the branch,★ spreading equally all around the branch and massed in "foxtails" near the ends of branches. "Branchlets clothed only at the extremities with long, dense, brushlike masses of foliage." Persist 10 to 15 years.
  Cones: Slender when closed, oblong ovate when open, 2½ to 5″ long, 1¾ to 2″ thick. Scales have thick tips with scar-like umbo. (Sargent says "scales armed with minute, incurved prickles.")
  Bark: Reddish brown, thin, smoothish but superficially checked into square plates. On old trees sometimes ¾″ thick. Surface scaly.
  Tree: In maturity 1 to 3′ × 40 to 60′, rarely 90′. The trunk is stocky and cone-shaped. In old trees trunk axis often projects through crown as dead and shining splinter point. Branches are stout, rather short with half-drooping branchlets.
  Distribution: *Spec.* Found at high elevations in small isolated groups usually at or near timberline from Scott Mountains in Siskiyou County to the southern Sierra Nevada on the Kern River watershed. At highest elevations often a low shrub, with wide-spreading, prostrate branches.
  Other Names: Balfour Pine.
  In General: The name "foxtail" comes from the bushy appearance of the foliage on young branches.

Ch45; HH70; J60; Sgt7; Sh5; Su39

U. S. Forest Service Photo

U. S. Forest Service Photo

U.S. Forest Service Photo

(*Pinus monophylla*)

Usual Occurrence:
    Geographical range—I to L inclusive
    Elevation range   —2,500 to 9,000′ (zones 2 and 3)
    Foliage   —Needles, attached singly

Needles: Attached singly, occasionally in pairs, $1\frac{1}{2}$ to 2″ long. ★*Perfectly circular* in section, stiff, incurving toward the branch and ending in an abrupt, sharp, prickly tip. Needles are light green and plentiful. Deciduous fourth to twelfth year. Foliage pale yellow-green, with whitish tinge. Faint rib-like grooves lengthwise of the needles.

Cones: Subglobose, $2\frac{1}{2}$ to $3\frac{1}{2}$″ in diameter. Scales thick, raised at ends into high, broad-based pyramids with flattened summits bearing a minute prickle. Seeds in pairs under each seed-bearing scale.

Bark: Dark brown, $\frac{3}{4}$″ thick, divided by deep irregular fissures into narrow, connected, flat ridges whose surface is broken into thin scales.

Tree: In maturity 12 to 15″ × 15 to 20′ (rarely 45′). Trunk often divides near the ground into several spreading stems. The trees are hardly more than bushes, thickset; foliage dense because of the plentiful needles. Appearance suggestive of an old apple tree.

Distribution: Dry desert slopes, some on western slope of Sierra but mainly on east side of the Sierra at elevations of 2,500 to 9,000′. Also Utah, Nevada, Arizona, and Lower California. Common on San Bernardino and San Jacinto Mountains.

Other Names: Piñon, Nut Pine, *Pinus cembroides* var. *monophylla*, Gray Pine, Nevada Nut Pine, One-leaf Piñon.

In General: The only one of the 17 pines of the Pacific slope whose needles are attached singly. Nuts from these trees are the ones sold in stores as "piñon nuts." Cones are gathered when mature but not opened, piled in stacks, and opened by slow fire. An exceedingly slow-growing tree.

Ch61; HH68; J72; Sgt10; Sh5; Su35

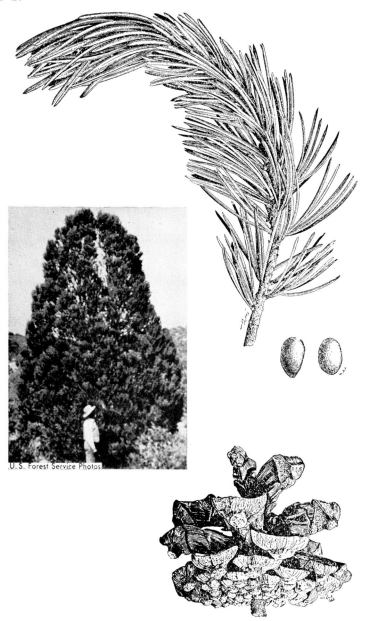

U.S. Forest Service Photos

FOURLEAF PINE   P-17
(*Pinus cembroides* var. *Parryana*)

Usual Occurrence:
>Geographical range—K and L
>Elevation range   —4,000 to 8,000′ (zones 2 and 3)
>Foliage   —Needles, in bundles of 4

Needles:★ In bundles of 1 to 5, usually 4, stout, incurved, pale blue-green with a whitish tinge. ¾ to 1⅝″ long. Needles fall in about three years.

Cones: Usually 1¼ to 2¼″ long. Very stubby to subglobose.

Bark: Usually ½ to ¾″ thick, reddish brown; has wide ridges covered with thick, plate-like scales.

Tree: "Merely a large bush of the desert slopes." A short-trunked, low tree, 15 to 30′ high, 10 to 16″ in diameter. Thick, spreading branches form a compact crown.

Distribution: Southern and Lower California in dry, mountain regions 4,000 to 8,000′.

Other Names: Nut Pine, Parry Pine, Parry's Nut Pine, Piñon, Parry's Piñon, *Pinus quadrifolia.*

In General: Nuts are used for food, but tree is too scarce to make them an important item in commerce. Young branches are coated at first with a soft, hair-like growth.

Ch65; HH69; J72; Sgt9; Sh5; Su33

(*Picea*)

Seven species of spruce are native to North America, and five of them are found in forests of the Pacific Coast.

Cones of the spruces mature in one season, are cylindrical or egg-shaped, and always droop from the branches. Most spruces bear their cones at the extreme top of the crown. A distinguishing characteristic of all spruce cones is the thin, papery cone scales, without prickles, very unlike the thick, strong cone scales of most conifers.

Distinguishing traits of spruces as a group are described effectively in a publication of the Canadian Forest Service from which the following quotation is taken:

The spruces can be readily distinguished from all other evergreens by their leaves (needles) which are sharp pointed and usually four sided in cross-section. They are single and stemless and each is borne on a tiny projection on the bark of the twig. In arrangement they are not distinctly two-ranked, as is the rule with the hemlocks and firs, but either bristle out from all sides or, on horizontal branches, are twisted and crowded densely toward the upper side of the twig.

The five species of spruce of which detailed descriptions follow are:

Engelmann Spruce............................... S-1
    (*Picea Engelmannii*)
Sitka Spruce.................................... S-2
    (*Picea sitchensis*)
Weeping Spruce................................. S-3
    (*Picea Breweriana*)
Black Spruce................................... S-4
    (*Picea Mariana*)
White Spruce................................... S-5
    (*Picea glauca*)

S-1

Canadian Forest Service

B. C. Forest Branch Photo

· 138 ·

(Picea Engelmannii)

Usual Occurrence:

Geographical range—A to G inclusive

Elevation range   —4,000 to 6,000' in Washington (zones 2 and 3)

Foliage   —Needles, attached singly

Needles: Four-angled, usually about 1" long, though often longer. They spread spirally on young branchlets that do not bear cones, but on cone-bearing twigs they crowd together upward, brush-like. Soft to the touch. Needle tips are characteristically short and flat. Branchlets are minutely hairy.

Cones: Size varies considerably; length ranges from 1 to almost 3". Cones grow in large numbers on the upper branches, first horizontally but become pendulous later. Cones are smaller than those of Sitka Spruce and fall in early autumn or winter. "Ends of cone scales are ordinarily squarish, sometimes pointed and notched."—Can

Bark: Scaly even on very young trees. On older trunks it is thin (¼ to ½" thick) and outwardly composed of very loosely attached scales.

Tree: Mature trees, in dense stands 18 to 36" × 80 to 100' or more. Larger in open stands, at very high elevations perhaps only 2 to 4' high. Narrow pyramidal crown of small branches. From all main horizontal branches hang numerous tassel-like side branchlets which give the tree a very compact appearance.

Distribution: Alaska southward to northern California—Peace River basin to Colorado, New Mexico, and Arizona. Elevation range:

Canada.................................	1,000 to 6,000'
Washington............................	4,000 to 6,000'
Arizona................................	8,500 to 11,000'
Colorado....	8,500 to 12,000'

Other Names: Upland Spruce, White Spruce, Western White Spruce, Mountain Spruce, Rocky Mountain Spruce.

In General: A slow-growing tree, very long lived even in unfavorable locations. On high, wind-swept crests specimens only 3 to 5" in diameter may be 150 to 200 years old. Large trees sometimes 500 to 600 years old. In appearance much similar to Sitka Spruce (S-2).

Although this tree usually grows at higher elevations than Sitka Spruce, the ranges sometimes overlap. Only an expert can distinguish the cones, so careful comparison of needles is necessary for distinction. On this point John A. Lee offers the suggestion: "Cut across several needles with a sharp knife: the section of Engelmann Spruce is distinctly four-angled and square-like while Sitka Spruce has relatively flat needles, less distinctly four-angled."

Can41; HH139; P66; Sgt38; Su78

Ore. Board of Forestry

Chas. Laidlaw Photo

U. S. Forest Service Photo

Usual Occurrence:

Geographical range—A to I inclusive

Elevation range   —0 to 3,500′ (zone 1)

Foliage   —Needles, attached singly

Needles: ½ to 1⅛″ long, flat, sharp pointed, stiff, very indistinctly four-angled,* practically all curved (P). Color, bright yellow-green. Have a bristly habit of standing out at right angles all around branchlets. Prickly to the touch.

Cones: 2 to 4″ long. Oval, short stalked, hang down conspicuously from the branches. Thin, papery, elliptic scales twice as long as their minutely toothed bracts. Fall every year in the autumn or early winter.

Bark: Reddish-brown, scaly on very young trees. On large trees, very thin (¼ to ½″ thick); has large, easily detached scales.

Tree: Mature trees 3 to 6′ × 80 to 125′ (sometimes 12 × 250′—Can). ★Bases of big trunks are swelled by enormous buttresses. In open stands or singly, it has a rapidly tapering bole with branches down to or near the ground. The crown is open, narrow, and sharp in its upper part but very broad at the base where the huge branches are 20 to 30′ long. Small branches lacy. Twigs of the year are always smooth and dark yellow-brown. "The branches are horizontal, frequently with many slender, hanging side-branches."—Can

Distribution: Northern Alaska to Mendocino County in northern California. Mostly along ocean shoreline only. Maximum distance inland is about 50 miles. Elevation range in Alaska is sea level to 3,500′. (Not above 1,000 or 2,000′ in Oregon.—JL) Contrary to usual custom of conifers, this one attains its highest elevations in the latitudes farthest north.

Other Names: Coast Spruce, Menzies Spruce, Western Spruce, Tideland Spruce (appropriately suggests the limited inland distribution).

In General: Noted for longevity. Trees 4 to 6′ × 150 to 180′ are 400 to 750 years old; trees 800 or 850 years old are found occasionally. A leading pulpwood. The largest and most imposing of all the spruces.

* A needle may be flat and at the same time four-angled if the cross-section has a flattened diamond shape.

Can41; HH137; P43; Sgt41; Sh17; Su81

U.S. Forest Service Photos

(Picea Breweriana)

Usual Occurrence:
      Geographical range—G, H
      Elevation range   —4,000 to 8,000' (zones 2 and 3)
      Foliage   —Needles, attached singly

Needles: Usually ¾ to 1⅛" long, attached singly, flat, or obscurely ridged into triangular shape, with the sharpest angle on the lower side.

Cones: About 3 to 3½" long, ¾ to 1¼" in diameter. Pendulous from straight, slender stalks. Mature in one season but fall slowly, many persisting until second autumn.

Bark: Dark brown, ¾" thick; has firmly attached scales.

Tree: In maturity 18 to 30" × 50 to 75'. Exceptional trees 100'. A thin, spike-like crown bears short, upturned branches. Midway the branches are horizontal, and the ★marked "weeping" habit of its lower branches distinguishes this tree from its associates. Unique characteristic of middle and lower branches is their numerous, very long, string-like branchlets; "slender, flexible, whip-like pendants, often only ¼" thick and 7 to 8' long."

Distribution: Southwest Oregon and northern California. Elevation 4,000 to 8,000'.

Other Names: Brewer's Spruce.

In General: A little-known and rare tree. Discovered in 1884.

HH143; Sgt40; Sh17; Su84

U. S. Forest Service Photo

BLACK SPRUCE   S-4

(*Picea Mariana*)

Usual Occurrence:

Geographical range—A
Elevation range   —Sea level to 3,500' (zone 1)
Foliage   —Needles, attached singly

Needles: Needles short and thick ($\frac{1}{4}$ to $\frac{3}{4}$" long), stand out on all sides of branchlets, have blunt tips and a four-angled cross-section. Foliage a deep blue-green, with a whitish tinge.

Cones: Small, only $\frac{1}{2}$ to $1\frac{1}{2}$" long, subglobose. Their habit of remaining ★firmly attached to the branches for very many years (20 or 30 years, sometimes) furnishes one of the most reliable means of distinguishing this species. Stems of the cones are very stout, firm, and curved downward or inward toward the branch. Cone scales are peculiarly stiff and resistant to pressure of the hand but easily broken if squeezed together. Margins of the scales are notched unlike those of the White Spruce, which are smooth.

Bark: Of old trees is thin ($\frac{1}{4}$ to $\frac{1}{2}$"), composed of small, ashy-brown scales.

Tree: In Alaska a small, stunted tree, often only 2 to 6' high, though occasionally 12 to 15' high. (Elsewhere ranges up to 1' in diameter and 50 to 80' high.) Crown characteristically open and irregular, extending to the ground. Branches are short, slim, and often distant from one another.

Distribution: Alaska and northeastern British Columbia (as well as in eastern Canada and the United States). Although essentially a swamp tree in its eastern range, in the North it is found in well-drained valleys and on stony slopes. It associates with Tamarack and Aspen.

Other Names: Red Spruce, Double Spruce, Water Spruce, Swamp Spruce, *Picea nigra.*

In General: This is mainly an eastern and far northern species, included as a Pacific tree only because of its occurrence in the interior of Alaska.

Can35; HH131; Sgt35; Su86

Canadian Forest Service

U. S. Forest Service Photo

Usual Occurrence:

Geographical range—A

Elevation range   —2,000 to 4,000′ (zone 2)

Foliage   —Needles, attached singly

Needles: Sharp-pointed, four-angled needles, ½ to ¾″ long, stand out all around the twigs except near ends of branchlets where they mass on upper side. Dense foliage, light blue-green color with whitish tinge. Young shoots and needles, when bruised, emit a fetid, skunk-like odor.

Cones: Usual length about 1¾″ (range is from 1 to nearly 2½″). Longer ★and more oval-shaped than the Black Spruce, they are pendulous and lightly attached and usually fall in autumn or by spring. When open and dry the cone scales are so thin and flexible that they can be squeezed together without breaking them, and when released they will spring back into place, quite unlike Black Spruce cones in this respect. Although cones are light brown after shedding the seeds, just at maturity they may be light grass-green, tinged with red or bright rose-red.

Bark: ¼ to ½″ thick, early broken into small, thin, pale ashy-brown scales.

Tree: In Alaska 12 to 20″ × 50 to 75′ in favorable locations. Also in stunted form only 8 to 20′ high. Branches long and thick. Commonly curve downward, then upward. A characteristic is the numerous, small, drooping side branchlets.

Distribution: Newfoundland to Hudson's Bay and northwestward to Alaska, reaching the Pacific at Bering Strait in north latitude 66° 44′. In Alaska at 2,000 to 4,000′. Also down along east side of Rocky Mountains into Montana at elevations of 3,000 to 5,000′.

Other Names: *Picea canadensis*, *Picea glauca* var. *albertiana*, Single Spruce, Skunk Spruce, Cat Spruce. The last name comes from the odor of young leaves when bruised, which resembles that of the polecat or skunk.

In General: Mainly a tree of the northeastern United States and Canada. Strictly speaking, this is not a tree of the "Pacific slope"; it is included here only because of its range in the interior (at least) of Alaska where it is the principal timber tree in the Yukon drainage basin.

Can36; HH133; Sgt37; Su88

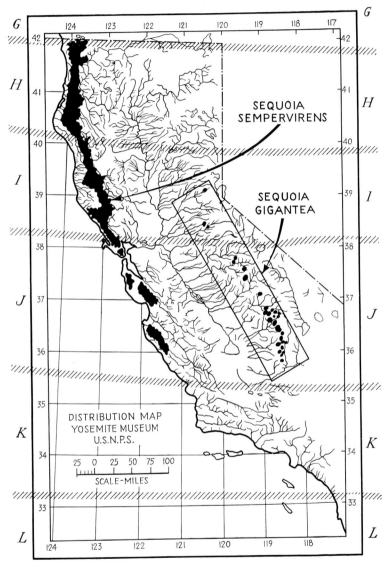

SEQUOIA
SEMPERVIRENS

SEQUOIA
GIGANTEA

DISTRIBUTION MAP
YOSEMITE MUSEUM
U.S.N.P.S.

25 0 25 50 75 100
SCALE-MILES

O<small>NLY</small> two species now remain of the genus Sequoia, though many more existed in prehistoric times. Remains of at least two Sequoias from which our species descended have been found in fossils of the Cretaceous and Tertiary periods, during which time they lived in the arctic zone. Because of the remarkably fire-resistant quality of the Sequoia bark there has been much speculation as to what caused the extinction of the other species of the family.

Although many of the largest trees have been wholly or partly destroyed, it is believed that trees of this species have attained ages of 4,000 and 5,000 years. The Sequoias of California are frequently referred to as the oldest living things in the world today. The name comes from an Indian chief, Sequoyah, a Cherokee, inventor of the Cherokee alphabet.

The two species of Sequoia of which detailed descriptions follow are:

Big Tree.. Se-1
    (*Sequoia gigantea*)
Redwood.. Se-2
    (*Sequoia sempervirens*)

Se-1

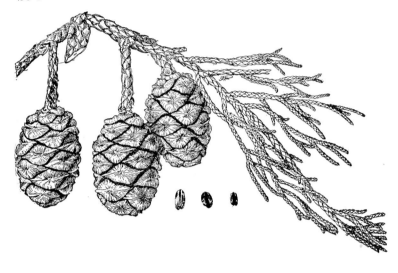

U. S. Forest Service Photo

· 150 ·

Usual Occurrence:

Geographical range—I, J

Elevation range   —5,000 to 8,500′ (zone 3)

Foliage   —Scale-like

Leaves: Small (⅛ to ¼ or ½″ on leaders), blue-green, awl-shaped, rigid scales which overlap one another and grow in sprays. Small twigs have short leaves; the larger ones have longer leaves; longest of all are the keenly pointed leaves on seedlings one to several years old.

Cones: 2 to 3¾″ long, 1½ to 2¼″ wide. Seeds are thin and flat, four to six under each cone scale. Cones mature the second summer. Seeds ⅛ to ¼″ long.

Bark: 1 to 2′ thick, red, stringy, extremely soft, almost spongy. Composed of fine fibers often frayed out by weather, squirrels, etc.

Tree: In maturity ordinarily 12 to 20′ × 200 to 280′. Some have diameters of 38′ or more. An exaggeration of base diameters is common because of the tendency to include in measurements the immense basal buttresses. In youth the tree forms a broad, sharp-pointed pyramid. After maturity the crown loses all semblance to youthful form and becomes a short, narrow, round-topped dome. Stem often devoid of branches for 150′ or more.

Distribution: *Spec.* Restricted generally to central California. Elevation 5,000 to 8,500′ on west side of the Sierra. (Sudworth lists location of 28 main groves.) See accompanying distribution map.

Other Names: *Sequoia Washingtoniana, Sequoia Wellingtonia,* Giant Sequoia.

In General: The "oldest living thing." Maximum life range 4,000 to 5,000 years. (Doubtful if any over 4,000 years now standing.) Wood and bark contain much tannin, as do drippings from cones which stain water a deep purple. Prostrate trunks lie on the ground for centuries with decay only in the sapwood.

Ch89; FW54; HH189; S30; Sgt62; Sh13; Sul39

Geo. J. Young Photo

Dimensions of Largest Living Big Trees

Determining the exact size of the largest living *Sequoia gigantea* was the assignment given to a committee of engineers some years ago by the Junior Chamber of Commerce of Fresno, Calif. The committee made measurements of numerous trees and finally submitted a report which was summarized by J. W. Jourdan, one of the committee, in an article published in *Engineering News-Record*, Feb. 18, 1932, p. 254. The following data are taken from that article.

Each tree was measured to determine (1) the height with reference to a mean base and (2) the restored volume including bark but exclusive of limbs. Restored volume was defined as existing volume plus the quantity lost by burns, the latter being confined largely to the tree bases. A tabular listing of results follows:

COMPARATIVE DIMENSIONS OF FOUR LARGEST BIG TREES

ITEM FOR COMPARISON	NAME OF TREE			
	GEN. SHERMAN	GEN. GRANT	BOOLE	HART
Height of top of trunk, ft..........	272.4	267.4	268.8	277.9
Volume, excluding limbs, cu. ft.....	49,660	43,038	39,974	32,607
Volume of burns, cu. ft............	350	2,194	1,420	1,639
Restored volume, cu. ft............	50,010	45,232	41,394	34,246
Perimeter of base on slope, ft.......	101.6	107.6	112.0	73.8
Perimeter (highest ground), ft......	88.0	92.9	90.3	68.7
Mean diameter of restored base, ft..	30.7	33.3	33.2	26.5
Mean diameter at 60 ft., in ft......	17.5	16.3	15.3	14.5
Mean diameter at 120 ft., in ft.....	17.0	15.0	13.9	12.9
Mean diameter at 180 ft., in ft.....	14.0	12.9	11.9	11.3
Height to first live limb, ft.........	99.7	83.8		
Height to first large limb, ft........	129.9	129.8	126.0	
Diameter first large limb, ft........	6.8	3.2		

Ntl. Park Service Photo

Additional Notes on the Big Trees

Because this is the most renowned of all California trees, space is devoted here to the following notes abstracted from the book "Big Trees" by Fry and White.

Rate of Growth: Sometimes the annular rings are so closely crowded together that 100 may be counted in a single inch. Again, individual rings may be as much as $\frac{1}{4}''$ thick. Because these trees live where each winter is a snow season and because they grow best when the snows are gone for the summer, it follows that years of greatest growth are years of longest summers, *i.e.*, years when snows melt early.

Other things being equal, this means maximum growth in summers following winters of minimum snowfall. The growing season of these trees may vary from 6 months to as little as 30 days because of temperature (as a factor in snow melting) and other climatic conditions.

Age: It is certain that the Big Tree lives to be 5,000 or 6,000 years old. The chances are overwhelming that they would die from some violent cause (fire, lightning, wind, landslide, etc.) before reaching senescence. In fact there is no record of death of a Big Tree from old age. The oldest ones now living have not lost their power of fertile seed production. Protected in parks they should live 10,000 years, or forever, so far as anyone knows.

Distinction between Big Tree and Redwood: "The chief characteristic of the Redwood is grace—of the Big Tree, majesty."

The foliage, of course, varies widely; the Redwood has needles attached singly, and the Big Tree has scale-like foliage. The Redwood is taller and occurs in heavy forest stands; the Big Tree is larger in diameter; its bark has a richer, deeper color; and most of the trees are in isolated groves. The Redwood grows from seed or from stump sprouts; the Big Tree reproduces only from seed.

Big Tree seed is extremely small—over 3,000 to the ounce. Under natural conditions perhaps only one seed in a million germinates, and a similarly small percentage of those which do germinate take root. Forest fires play an important part in providing likely seeding ground where new trees may start.

Squirrel harvests provide a most convenient source of Big Tree seed. Thirty-eight barley sacks of cones were taken from a single cache made by one squirrel in a 12-day period. These cones yielded 26 lb. of seed.

Fire-resistant Bark: Single fires rarely kill a Big Tree because of the fire resistant bark, but succeeding fires eat away material previously killed by fire. Debris from other trees, more particularly the inflammable, resinous wood of firs and pines, piled about Big Tree bases have caused the greatest fire hazard to this species.

A certain Big Tree 16 ft. in diameter was subjected to a 7-day fire of fir logs on one side of its base. This so "cooked" the wood fibers within the trunk that sap flow was cut off in one-fourth of the sap-flow area. That year the entire tree continued to thrive, living on nourishment within its huge bulk. Next season the topmost 30 ft. died. Thirteen years later a second fire ate away the previously burned portion and reduced the sap-flow area to one-third the original. As a result, in the following season another 15 ft. of the top withered and died. "*Seventy five per cent of dead tops are caused by basal fire scars.*"

U.S. Forest Service Photo

W. L. Huber Photo

REDWOOD Se-2

(Sequoia sempervirens)

Usual Occurrence:

    Geographical range—G to J inclusive

    Elevation range   —0 to 3,000′ (zone 1)

    Foliage   —Needles, attached singly

Needles: Flat, sharp-pointed, stiff, of unequal length, and lengths of $\frac{1}{3}$ to 1″ may occur on the same twig. Have a prominent midrib, and show a flat-ranked spray by reason of a half turn at the base. On side twigs of lower branches and on young saplings, needles stand out in two lines on opposite sides of twig; on the main stems they vary in length down to short scale-like forms, sometimes pressed closely to the branch. Often cling to branches a year or two after they are dead. Under sides of needles usually whitish, in contrast with dark green of upper surface. Needle stems are very short. Foliage of young growth has a resemblance to Big Tree foliage. Typical sprays are in segments which show annual growth.

Cones: Even smaller than those of the Big Tree, only $\frac{3}{4}$ to 1″ long. Seed thin and flat. Cones mature in one year. Four or five seeds under each cone scale.

Bark: Of old trunks 8 to 12″ or more thick, widely furrowed, and ridged at base in rounded, rich brown, stringy strands.

Tree: In maturity 8 to 12 or 15′ × 190 to 280′. Sometimes 300′ or more. Grows taller than the Big Tree but has less trunk diameter and is more tapering.

Distribution: From Chetco River, Oregon (8 miles north of California-Oregon state line), southward to Monterey County, California. Generally from sea level to about elevation 2,500′. Mainly on seaward slopes and in fog belt. Few in Oregon, mainly a California tree. Shinn says (p. 13): "Habitat is belt 450 mi. long on seaward side Coast Range Mountains from southern Oregon to Santa Lucia Mountains in Monterey County. Greatest distance inland, 30 mi. Never grows naturally out of reach of the ocean fogs." See accompanying distribution map.

Other Names: Coast Redwood.

In General: Age average is much less than the Big Tree. A Redwood 20′ in diameter and 350′ high gave a ring count of 1,000. Oldest ring count about 1,400 years.

HH185; P65; S19; Sgt61; Sh13; Sul45

Se-2

About 1932 the California Park Board commissioned E. P. French, superintendent of the northwest district, to make a search for the tallest tree in the redwood belt.   After several months, during which he measured hundreds of trees, French reported that a tree at Dyerville measuring 364' high was the tallest.   This tree now is known as the "Founders Tree" in honor of Dr. John C. Merriam, Madison Grant, and Dr. Henry Fairfield Osborn, founders of the "Save the Redwoods League."   Dimensions of other large Redwoods are given in the table.

DIMENSIONS OF LARGE REDWOODS
(Data from California State Division of Parks, Sept. 4, 1937)

LOCATION	CIRCUM-FER-ENCE ON GROUND	DIAM-ETER BREAST HIGH	HEIGHT, FT.	TIMBER, FT., BOARD MEASURE	
				STAND	MILL CUT
Del Norte State Park (Stout Memorial Grove)	62' 3"	16' 6"	340	. . . .	130,800
Humboldt State Park (¾ mile north of Elk Grove Camp, on Prairie Creek)	90'	17' 7"	200	. . . .	128,000
Bull Creek Flat (4 miles west of Dyerville)	72'	16' 6"	345	235,000	154,000
Dyerville Flat (tallest Red-wood)	47'	. . . .	364	. . . .	125,000
California Redwood Park:					
Father Tree	66' 9"	16' 10"	250	177,000	133,000
Mother Tree	70'	15' 3"	329	141,345	101,960
Santa Clara Tree	65' 6"	17' 9"	240	200,000	145,000
North of Klamath-Coulter (tree advertised as world's largest)	71'	16' 2"	280	. . . .	84,000

To

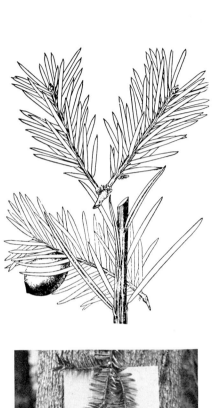

California Nutmeg   To
(*Torreya californica*)*

Usual Occurrence:

    Geographical range—H, to K inclusive

    Elevation range   —0 to 6,000′ (zones 1 and 2)

    Foliage   —Needles, attached singly

Needles: Flat, shining, sharply pointed, rigid, $1\frac{1}{4}$ to 3″ long. Needles attach uniformly to branchlets so as to form a two-ranked, flat spray. Lustrous on upper surface, paler green to whitish below.

Fruit: The seed kernel suggests the nutmeg of commerce (also resembles olive or small plum), green in color when ripe, streaked with purple. $1\frac{1}{8}$ to $1\frac{3}{4}$″ long. Shell of seed longitudinally grooved.

Bark: $\frac{1}{3}$ to $\frac{1}{2}$″ thick, rather soft, finely checked seams, green on the younger branches but yellows with age. Sometimes gray-brown, tinged with orange. Elongated, loose scales are common.

Tree: In maturity $1\frac{1}{2}$ to 3′ × 15 to 50′, rarely 4 × 100′. Slender branches stand out rather straight from the trunk in formal circles and are somewhat drooping at their extremities. Trunks are rarely straight, in maturity are clear of branches for two-thirds of the height.

Distribution: *Spec.* On west slopes of the Sierra and in the Coast Range. From Lake and Mendocino Counties on the north to Kern County on the south, but never in any considerable quantity. Prefers cool, shady canyons or sheltered slopes. On western slopes of the Sierra usual elevation range is 3,000 to 5,000′; along the coast the elevation range extends down to sea level.

Other Names: Yew, Stinking Yew, Stinking Cedar, Nutmeg Tree, California False Nutmeg, *Tumion Californicum.*

In General: A rare tree, called "Nutmeg" from the fancied resemblance of its seed kernels to the nutmeg of commerce, which belongs to a different and unrelated family of broadleaf plants. ★A sharp, aromatic, and disagreeable odor is emitted by needles or branchlets when bruised; hence the name "Stinking Cedar." Not a cone bearer, but included here because it is likely to be mistaken for one.

* Not a cone bearer.

HH226; J127; Sgt92; Sh17; Su191

Y

WESTERN YEW   Y
(*Taxus brevifolia*)*

Usual Occurrence:

      Geographical range—A to I inclusive

      Elevation range   —0 to 6,000′ (zones 1, 2, and 3)

      Foliage   —Needles attached singly

Needles: ½ to 1″ long about $\frac{1}{16}$″ wide; flat, rounded ends; deep, yellow-green above; paler below. Soft to the touch, have stout midribs. Persistent 5 to 12 years.

Fruit: This species does not bear cones but has a small, bright red fruit about ⅓″ long which is palatable and often is eaten by birds. The fruit resembles the red huckleberry, but the seed protrudes from the fleshy covering and always is on the underside of branchlets.

Bark: About ¼″ thick, composed of papery, purple, easily detached scales. Beneath the scales the newer bark is clear rose-red or purple-red.

Tree: In maturity 6 to 12″ × 20 to 30′ (rarely 80′). Inland, away from the coast, the tendency is to smaller size; sometimes shrubby. Trunks are straight and fluted by an apparent infolding of the surface, frequently unsymmetrical, one diameter much exceeding the other. Slender branches, straight, somewhat drooping. Very slender branchlets hang down giving a weeping appearance.

Distribution: Along the coast ranges from Alaska to central California, eastward to Montana. Grows in moist locations. Found near Monterey Bay and on western slopes of Sierra Nevada. Elevation range in California is sea level to 6,000′.

Other Names: Yew, Pacific Yew, Mountain Mahogany.

In General: Not a cone bearer, but included here because it is likely to be mistaken for one.

* Not a cone bearer.

Can72; HH228; P66; Sgt93; Sh17; Su194

GLOSSARY

bole—the main trunk or stem of a tree.

bract—a modified or undeveloped leaf or organ attached to or between the scales of cones.

catkin—a densely flowered, scaly spike which falls whole after flowering or after maturity. Also applied to flowering cones.

crown—the branches and foliage of a tree or shrub. As used in describing the appearance of the tree as a whole, it means the entire tree above the base of the trunk.

dendrology—the branch of botany dealing with trees.

glaucous—overcast with a whitish bloom, as on a plum.

glandular—provided with gland-like protuberances on the surface or partly imbedded in the surface.

globose—globular, or nearly so.

morphology—the branch of biology dealing with the form and structure of animals and plants.

ovate
ovoid } —broad and tapering to a narrow apex, egg-shaped.

ovule—the part of the flower that becomes a seed.

silva—the forest trees of a region collectively.

stomata—breathing pores in the epidermis of needles connecting internal cavities with the external air.

subglobose—somewhat less rounded than would justify the term globose.

umbo—a certain protuberance or point. Here applied to formations on the tips of cone scales.

whorl—radial from a common point. A circle of flowers, branches or other growths about the same point on the axis, like the spokes of a wheel around the hub.

Because of the very frequent use of the word "species" in this manual the beginner may find it helpful if the distinctions between genus, species, and variety are made clear so that he will not misuse or confuse these terms.

A *genus* is a group of one or more related species classified separately because this group differs from other groups in a fundamental way.

A *species* is a group of lower order than a genus and refers to a single distinct type, *i.e.*, trees that have distinctive characteristics in common.

A *variety* is a group of lower order than a species, indicating relation by descent and distinction from similar groups only by traits too slight to constitute a separate species.

These definitions will become clearer from the following statements: The genus pine includes many species such as Yellow Pine and Sugar Pine, and among these species are some in which there are more than one variety. For example, some authors distinguish the beach variety of Lodgepole Pine (P-4) from the mountain variety. Both varieties belong to the species Lodgepole Pine which is one of the many species included in the genus "pine."

INDEX

(Symbols, alphabetically arranged, are used in place of page numbers)

· 168 ·